From Mum
Christmas 1996

A
MENSA
PUZZLE BOOK

THE MENSA
PUZZLE BOOK

VICTOR SEREBRIAKOFF
INTERNATIONAL CHAIRMAN OF MENSA

CHANCELLOR
PRESS

First Published in Great Britain by Frederick Muller
under the titles
A Mensa Puzzle Book © 1982 Victor Serebriakoff
and *A Second Mensa Puzzle Book* © Victor Serebriakoff

This omnibus edition published in 1991 by Chancellor Press
an imprint of Reed Consumer Books Ltd
Michelin House, 81 Fulham Road, London SW3 6RB
and Auckland, Melbourne, Singapore and Toronto

Reprinted 1992, 1993, 1994, 1995

ISBN 1 85051 690 1

A CIP catalogue record for this book is available from
the British Library

Printed and bound in Great Britain by Bath Press

ACKNOWLEDGEMENTS

I want to thank my puzzle-wise wife, Win, my son, Mark and his wife, Liz, for a lot of help in composing puzzles and correcting mistakes.

To some extent, all ventures by Mensans are joint ventures, you get a lot of help from your Mensa friends. In particular I thank my collaborator and co-author of Part 2, Ken Russell and also Jonathan Causer, who both worked so hard to provide a puzzle column in MENSA the British Mensa magazine when I was Editor. This is the source of many of these puzzles.

I also thank the British Mensa Chairman Sir Clive Sinclair and the Committee, Howard Neil, Arthur C. Clarke, Madsen Pirie, John Williams of Belfast Mensa, Harold Gale, Harper Fowley (a fellow Kentucky Colonel who humbles me by rejecting Feghoots), Cecilie Irgens of Norwegian Mensa, who was a willing helper on her computer, my friend Isaac Asimov, from whose works I have frequently borrowed, the late Ernst Rosenthal, D. St. P. Barnard, and my hundreds of Mensa correspondents who infuriate me by posting off the correct answers to my monthly puzzles in the British Mensa Newsletter with a postmark which shows they must have answered the question before they saw it. Many of them have been very helpful with advice and suggestions.

Victor Serebriakoff
London, 1991

About Mensa

To be a Mensa member is to be a certified puzzle solver. We are, we Mensans, the whole lot of us dedicated, masochistic, puzzle fiends. Our hundreds of journals, international, national and local, are full of nasty, tricky, unhelpful, devious puzzles, posers, enigmas, quizzes and problems. It has been calculated that the brain-hours we 60,000 Mensans devote each year to puzzles, would, if we could ever agree on anything and turn our minds to systematic co-operation, solve all the world's social, political, economic and cultural problems — and produce a world of excruciatingly boring perfection. The need for interesting puzzles would increase a thousand-fold!

However, Mensa has no dogma. Fortunately we agree on nothing except that we delight in each others provoking, stimulating company. So we shall continue to throw up, as we should, a wide variety, of views, ideas, proposals and hypotheses for general acceptance or rejection.

Perhaps you would like to know more about this odd bunch.

What is Mensa?

Mensa is a unique society. It is, basically, a social club — but a social club different from others. The only qualification for membership is a high score on an intelligence test. One person in fifty should qualify for membership; these people will come from all walks of life and have a wide variety of interests and occupations.

Mensa is the latin word for table: we are a round-table society where no one has special precedence. We fill a void for many intelligent people otherwise cut off from contact with other good minds — contact that is important to them, but elusive in modern society. Beside being an origin of many new friendships, we provide members with a receptive but critical audience on which to try out new ideas.

Mensa is protean: its most visible feature is its diversity. It crosses the often artificial barriers which separate people from each other. It recruits, not like other societies by persuading people to think as they do, or by searching for a particular narrow common interest, but by scientifically selecting people who are able to think for themselves. Yet, although there appears little common ground and little surface agreement between members, we find there is an underlying unity which gives an unexpected strength to the society.

Mensa has three aims: social contact between intelligent people; research in psychology and the social sciences; and the identification and fostering of human intelligence. Mensa is an international society; it has over 60,000 members. We have members of almost every occupation — businessmen, clerks, doctors, editors, factory workers, farm labourers, housewives, lawyers, policemen, politicians, soldiers, scientists, students, teachers — and of almost every age.

Enquiries and applications to:

INTERNATIONAL MENSA
Bond House
St John's Square
Wolverhampton WV2 4AH
England.

To Mensa, the invigorating, stimulating, provoking soil where my
mind grows.

NOTE TO THE READER:

There are two sets of answers which follow on directly from
the puzzles in Parts I and II respectively. In each case, the
answer is given a different number and is arranged in a
different order to that of the problem in order to minimise
'inadvertent peeking' at the solutions.

CONTENTS

Starting Something You Cannot Finish

An Ordeal of Foul Feghoots

I Could Have Kicked Myself 74

Answering the Unanswerable Question 86

The Problems Problem

Our problems are man-made, therefore they may be resolved by man. And man can be as big as he wants. No problem of human destiny is beyond human beings.

John F. Kennedy,
address to The American University,
Washington, D.C., 10th June 1963.

The activity upon which I am shamelessly engaged is anti-social at best, and at its worst can be said to be evil. "Are there not enough problems in the world?" you might reasonably ask, "without sitting down, deliberately, to compose more?"

"Tee hee", or perhaps on second thoughts, "Nyeh! nyeh!" I reply. "There are! There are!" But I tempt you and dare you and provoke you to spend time and tax your poor brains on these. They are subtly composed and designed to look easy but once entrapped, you will be hooked and possessed by an obsessive, uncontainable urge to find the answer for yourself.

Draw back now if you can because, obstinate in wickedness, I intend no mercy. I shall employ all the evil schemes, tricks and underhand dodges of the puzzle-composer's art to confuse, disturb, muddle and trick you. You are entering a minefield. There are booby-traps everywhere.

16

Even those hardy few who come through safely to the end of the book, having, to my fury, solved all or most of the problems, shouldn't gloat too much. I am busily scribbling away and before you know it there will be another series of wickedly difficult puzzles to perplex and distress you. Meanwhile, grinning with fiendish pleasure, I see you scratching your head, scribbling on the insides of cigarette packets as you try vainly to feed your addiction. Steeped in wickedness I shall merely laugh. Be warned! Venture no further unless you take a masochistic pleasure in torturing your mind. If you read on, I have every excuse. After all it is sadistic not to torture masochists.

A Subtle and Immoral Trick

A subtle and immoral way to vex and thwart a sportsman or athlete is to ask him to "analyse" his skills. If you think about what your body is doing when you play tennis, you will serve double faults and net every ball.

So, assuming this works for problem solving, let my first problem be:

How Do We Solve Problems?

Let us first think about what a problem is. The elements of a problem situation are: that there is an informational input to start with; some options concerning the relevant optimum behavioural output and some uncertainty regarding those options. The task is that of reducing the options to those few, or more usually that one, which is optimum and initiating action to apply or pass on the solution. The output behaviour may be very simple, making a pencil tick, or saying some words but we shall not know that a problem has been solved until someone *behaves* in some way. So the basic essence of a problem is that of deciding between options.

For any situation to merit the name problem there must be some real doubts about the behavioural options. If there is no doubt and the optimum answer is obvious, the input does not merit the name "problem".

So the processes seem to be:

1. INPUT. What computer people call data-capture, receiving and storing an input of information. This might include arranging it in an optimal fashion.

2. OPTION GENERATION. Finding or originating a set of optional hypotheses, a set of contexts, or frames of reference which can make sense of the data.

3. DECISION MAKING. Reducing the options by elimination until the correct or best answer or answers have been isolated. (Many problems have several valid answers.)

4. ANSWERING. Verbal behaviour to communicate the chosen option or motor behaviour to actuate it.

Now I know that the above is not a usual way to look at problems and I expect some readers will be thinking of problem-solving as a logical chain-process with many links of premise leading to a conclusion. So let me deal with this.

Chain-like logical processes are the kind of problem-solving which the computer does best and the human mind does worst. The human mind excels at judgment, balancing odds. Now I claim that most problem-solving cases fit the pattern I have described and do not fit the traditional view that problem-solving is simply a matter of picking the right path along a logical chain. I argue that problem-solving, which consists in making the correct link at a number of successive steps is, in fact, a slowed-down version of choosing between many options. At each step there is a correct choice and a large or infinite number of incorrect ones. In logical problems it is only if the correct choice is made at each and every step that the right conclusion will be reached. The number of possible wrong paths at various points in time in most cases is enormous. In Judgment problems there are often many solutions.

Why are Puzzles Fun for Some People?

You will have observed, no doubt, as I have, that for most people thinking is a strategy of last resort. They live up to the motto: "if all else fails — start thinking". But there are an odd minority of curious people, outsiders like you and me who actually *enjoy* puzzles.

I have taken a somewhat jokey approach to my puzzle setting and there is a semantic link between puzzles and humour. There is no doubt that the solution of puzzles gives pleasure, otherwise why are you reading this book? This fact is odd and interesting. When any animal solves the problems set to it by its environment, it is rewarded by success, it gains food, a mate, an improved habitat or some other advantage. But it is almost certainly true that while you are spending your time on this puzzle, you might have been doing something which would be more to your advantage from the point of view of survival. So from that point of view, doing puzzles is like smoking or drinking, pleasurable without being advantageous.

So — I tempt you, forward into the morass, the minefield — advance — But BEWARE YOU HAVE BEEN WARNED!

The Answers

Puzzle books are naturally full of problems but the whole class of books has its own problem.

The problem lies in looking up the answers.

In looking up the answer to one problem, it is difficult not to get a sneaky peek at the answers to others.

I have tried to overcome this by giving each problem a different answer number and arranging the answers in a different order from that of the problems. I hope this underhand trick will maximise your difficulties.

PART I

PROBLEMS, POSERS, PUZZLES AND PASTIMES

by VICTOR SEREBRIAKOFF
INTERNATIONAL CHAIRMAN OF MENSA

A Tribulation of Torturing Teasers

Problems are only opportunities in work clothes.   *Henry J. Kaiser*

T.1   Sorting Scribbles

The first activity of Mind in contact with the World is that of sorting scribble. All inputs are meaningless until they have been classified. There is the story of the tramp who applied to a farmer for a hand-out.

"Mend that fence and hoe those turnips first," said the heartless farmer. The tramp proved to be a quick and efficient worker, was fed well and given more work next day. After a week the farmer became enthusiastic. "Keep on like this and you've a regular job."

"A regular job! Marvellous, I'll do anything!"

In a few days all the more obvious chores had been finished by the fast-working vagrant. The farmer put him on wages and gave him an easy job for the Saturday. "You must be tired out. Just spend your morning sorting those potatoes, about a quarter of them are bad."

"Anything, Guv, I love working for you, Guv!" But an hour later the tramp came and turned the job in. "I can't stand it," he said.

"What's the trouble? I thought it was an easy job."

"It's making them decisions."

You are invited to torture yourself similarly by trying to classify these scribbles.

How many types of scribble? List the letters according to scribble type.

See Answer No. 46.

T.2   Motor Boat

A man takes his motor boat to go down a river to his pub. Going with the current he can cover the two kilometres in two minutes. Returning against the current, which is steady, it takes him four minutes. How long does it take him at slack water when there is no current?

See Answer No. 34.

25

T.3 Klondyke

When the prospectors arrived in the Klondyke there was a great shortage of some materials and a surplus of others. There was masses of string and rope but no measuring instruments; they had to find some method of allocating land fairly and equally. One authority hit on the rather peculiar idea of issuing each prospector with an equal length of rope. The prospector was entitled to claim all the land that he could enclose with the rope when it was formed into a loop. This idiotic rule led to a mad scramble and a great deal of confusion on the first day and so the second day a new rule was introduced. The piece of land enclosed must fit in with other claims, there must be no spaces between claims.

The prospectors started to drift into groups, according to different methods of forming an enclosed space with a standard loop, and it soon emerged that one group had hit upon a way which optimised the size of each claim and which still remained within the rules. The solver must put himself in the position of the thinker for the successful group — he must advance and justify his scheme.

See Answer No. 98.

T.4 Message from an Incommunicado

However much authorities try, it seems to be impossible to prevent news from travelling between cells in prisons and that is why the rulers of a world power whose name I have forgotten went to such extremes when they found that one of their scientists, one in possession of secrets of overwhelming importance, was an agent for an unfriendly foreign power.

He was an extremely subtle and tricky character but they had great hopes that they would break him or "turn" him. The rulers suspected that other agents may have penetrated the prison where he was held but they meant to make it impossible for him to transmit any information from his cell.

He was kept naked, in a small box-like cell, which was suspended from springs in a deep vault in such a way that no knocking or any other kind of sound could be emitted. His food, his drink and other necessities went into the cell under strict supervision by trustworthy jailers. His food waste, urine, excrement and even his hair and nail clippings were all handled by these same people and disposed of in such a way that no one was able to glean a coded message from their arrangements.

Careful monitoring equipment made quite sure that no radiant signal of any kind emerged from the inner cell. No books or papers or indeed any thing other than the carefully monitored food, drink and toilet necessities passed out of the cell and all these were handled as described.

You will be utterly astonished and amazed (or not as the case may be), when I tell you, after this build-up, that despite all these precautions, a signalling system was established and the tricky prisoner using a pre-arranged code, managed to transmit messages to accomplices on the prison staff but outside the hidden circle of the trusted people who were his jailers. How did he communicate?

See Answer No. 25.

T.5 The Evil Ways of Augustus Henry Simpkins

Augustus Henry Simpkins was the bottom, he was a practical joker and a more vicious, scheming, wicked example of the breed did not exist.

Let me recount just one incident. I was with him when it happened. He went into a grocer's shop and ordered a tin of tomatoes.

"Thirty-eight pence, sir," said the assistant, handing him the tin.

Simpkins (picking the tin up): "No, no, not those, I want tomatoes."

Assistant: "But they are tomatoes, sir, look, at the label."

Simpkins (shaking the tin and listening to it): "No, no, they're not tomatoes, they're peaches."

Assistant: "Excuse me, sir, perhaps you can't read, I can assure you that those are tomatoes. They're quite clearly labelled."

Simpkins: "I certainly can read and I can certainly tell the difference between tinned tomatoes and tinned peaches and those are tinned peaches. Can I have some tomatoes, please."

The assistant brought the manager and a similar argument went on for some time. Eventually Simpkins offers to bet the manager that the tin contains peaches and the manager, intrigued and anxious to win a fiver, produces a tin opener and opens the tin to find that it is in fact peaches.

The solver is set the harsh problem of explaining how Simpkins knew enough to be confident in his bet.

When you have solved this, you should proceed to puzzle No. T27 where you will be confronted with an even more difficult problem on the same nasty lines.

See Answer No. 32.

T.6 Dicing

In the gambling hells of Las Vegas you can find tables of apparently serious people shooting craps, throwing dice, all day.

It is even more extraordinary to see those who sit at the games trying to work out systems by carefully recording the way the dice fall. This activity which can surely qualify as the most boring in the world is pursued with dedication, perseverance and passion at great expense by the worshippers at that Shrine of Luck. One of them became convinced that it was not the sum of the face values of the two dice but the difference between them which mattered. He recorded these for years. He discovered, over his many years of observation that a certain difference happened once every eighteen throws on average and another difference which happens once every nine throws on average. What were the differences concerned?

See Answer No. 44.

T.7 Telling the Time with a Trombone

Many and various are the methods by which men have told the time over the years: dripping water clocks, sundials, hourglasses, clockwork and electronics. The world had to wait for me to be born before, in a blinding flash, it was revealed that one could tell the time with a trombone.

After a drinking and gambling session one summer night in my dissolute youth, Georgie and I were sleeping quietly in a park because the landlady used to lock us out after twelve. I woke to find that I had acquired this trombone somewhere — probably won it in a bet. I woke Georgie and suggested that we go to the Crown for a livener.

"You're as daft as a brush! The pubs closed hours ago."

I asked him what the time was.

"Lost my watch in the brag game."

"Mine has stopped and it's too dark to see it anyway."

Then the stroke of genius.

"I know what," I said, "I can tell the time with this trombone."

"Victor, you excel. You display excellence in idiocy. How can you tell the time with a trombone?"

"I'll show you," I said.

We walked (so to speak) from the park into a street where every light was out. I knew how to get a sound out of a trumpet and soon had the trombone working a treat. ("Treat" may not be *le mot juste*.) I will not claim that the music was sweet or, to revive a lost negative, cordant, but it *was* loud, *very* loud. Georgie, who is tone deaf, joined in with the loud braying he usually produced in the context of singing.

Several bedroom lights came on and a window flew up. A face contorted with rage appeared and, in a voice somewhere between a scream and a roar, an honest citizen reasonably asked to know: "What's all this racket at half past three in the morning?"

"There," I said to Georgie as we stumbled uncertainly on, "I told you I could tell the time with a trombone. The exact time is between two and three precisely."

"Clot," he said.

No-one appreciates a pioneer genius until years later.

I address the reader. Yes, you — you ought to know but almost certainly do *not* know the answer to this next question. It is a disgrace. Will you *never* learn. There is something you have observed thousands of times yet you simply haven't troubled to notice. And it is long odds against your being able to calculate it with reasonable accuracy.

Quite a number of times a day on a traditional clock the axis of the hour hand is exacly aligned with the axis of the minute hand. My question is:

A. What *precisely* is the interval in time between this event on two successive occasions. The answer must be exact!

See Answer No. 49.

B. To make sure you have really got it right, at exactly what moment between 6 o'clock and 7 o'clock are the hands aligned? Answer to the nearest millisecond.

See Answer No. 55.

T.8 Four-Letter Words

Four-letter words are generally that set of Anglo-Saxon expressions which are obscene, indecorous or offensive. However, looked at from an international point of view, it might have worked out that the expression "four-letter words", might be thought to have a meaning very far indeed from such profanities.

The solver is invited to find the context in which the expression might be used in a very different way.

See Answer No. 60.

T.9 Twisting My Word

Write down a four-letter word that is the same read forward, backwards or upside down.

See Answer No. 64.

T.10 How to Put a Bulge on a Bottom

This is an industrial problem that, long ago, was solved. It is not really one that requires know-how, it is just a question of intelligence.

The illustration overleaf shows the earpiece of an old-fashioned telephone. These were made of brass and the method was to press them from flat brass sheet. A round disc was first cut and then, by successive stages of pressing, with different presses and dyes, it was made into a shallow cup, annealed again, and so by successive stages to a deep tube like the earpiece except for the bulb on the end. In each case the press tool formed the inside and the dye formed the outside of the shape.

The problem is: how was the bulb on the end formed? An opening dye to allow the finished shape to be removed can easily be designed but a press tool to enter the narrow part of the tube, expand to press the bulb and then retract to be withdrawn is not possible within the strength limitations.

So how was the bulb formed?

See Answer No. 69.

THE STAGES OF PRESSING AN EARPHONE

Flat Plate

The Bulge

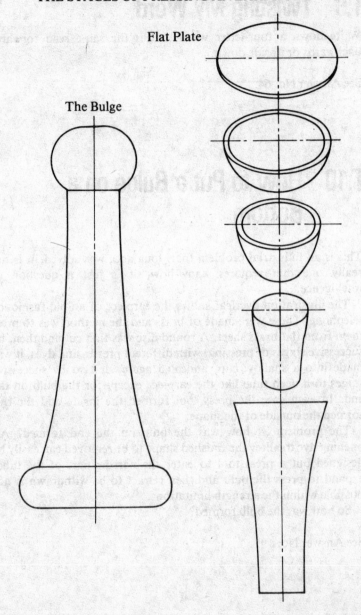

T.11   Concrete Without Shuttering

Here is another industrial puzzle where the solution is open to the enquiring, intelligent mind.

To make a concrete structure, it is normal to employ wooden or metal shuttering, boards or sheets, which are constructued to form the mould into which the concrete is poured.

Concrete has very little strength in tension or bending but is strong in compression. A dome is designed for construction in stone which has similar properties.

You are an engineer in a far-off, troubled land and you have to make a large, concrete air-raid shelter. You have any amount of labour, of concrete, of water and the soil is sand. You have wheelbarrows and shovels but you have nothing else except what is needed to sustain your labour force.

How do you build your air-raid shelter?

See Answer No. 74.

T.12   Cooked Books

I am a man with few prejudices and despite a business career I know some accountants whom I count as friends. You will be even more puzzled at my open-hearted tolerance when you hear the little rhyme that an accountant friend used to recite when trying to get to the bottom of inexplicable discrepancies:

"Hey diddle diddle
The cat and the adjustment."

As a technologist, I was used to the more orthodox form of arithmetic where one is manipulating numbers and signs so as to find the solution, a number one needs to know. The art of book-cookery is a sort of anti-arithmetic where you start with the answer and arrange the arithmetic to suit.

Tempting the solver into even more evil ways, I invite you to join this discreditable activity. You are invited to fiddle the arithmetic to produce the predetermined answer and if you are good at it you only have your moral scruples between you and the life of a swindler.

Your input is simply the figure 2 five times written thus:
$$2\ 2\ 2\ 2\ 2 = x$$
You also are given the four arithmetic signs and nothing else:
$$+, -, \times, \div$$
Problem A: Arrange the four signs in the four spaces between the figures in the equation so that the result is x = 4. There are *two* ways to do it. What are they?

See Answer No. 79.

Problem B: These particular books do not cook all that easily, there seems to be a bias towards some results. How many different recipes give the answer x = 2?

See Answer No. 84.

Problem C: What other values may x have?

See Answer No. 88.

T.13 All Bounce

This story is a good illustration of changes in standards.

It concerns an indignant mother who sued the local council because they had deliberately taken action which resulted in her son having his nose broken by a flying brick. The boy was in the habit of throwing a brick through the glass cover of a certain lamp-post whenever it was replaced and the council, apparently with malice aforethought, and in a very underhand way, replaced the panes of glass with stiff plastic. The brick bounced back and injured the poor child. The parents are taking legal action against the council.

This is not the only problem caused by bouncing.

A train of infinite mass is proceeding along a track at 60 mph and on the front of it there is a perfectly elastic metal plate. Another amiable boy decided that it would be a good idea to throw a metal ball, which again is perfectly elastic, at the train from a bridge under which it is to pass. He does so, and the ball flies towards the train at 60 mph. The ball bounces back off the plate and fortunately missed the boy, thus saving the railway company a large sum in damages. But the problem is, if it had hit the boy, at what speed would it have been travelling? We can ignore friction with the air, gravity and other such irritating complications.

See Answer No. 92.

T.14 The Naughty Young Twister

I am a brazenly open puzzle-setter, old and set in my wicked ways. But some take up the evil practice when they are mere children. You will be appalled at the nastiness of schoolboy Jenkins.

The teacher gave every child in the class a strip of paper, 2 cm wide and 20 cm long. "Now children, I want you to lay your strips of paper in front of you and I want you to write a very long number going all along the piece on one side."

The children got busy and in a minute the teacher said, "Have you finished? You've got a long number all along one side of the piece and the other side has nothing written on it. Now I want you to write a long line of *letters* on the other side. Does everybody understand?"

Everybody did apparently except our villain, a nasty grubby little boy. "Please, Teacher, I can't, please, Teacher, please."

"It's always you, isn't it, Jenkins? It's always different with you. Everybody else can do it but you can't do it. Why can't you do it, Jenkins?"

"Please, Teacher, please, there's only one side to my piece of paper and it's all full up with the numbers like you told me Teacher, please."

The teacher sighed with exhausted patience. "What is it now, Jenkins, are you telling me that *your* piece of paper has only got one side and everybody else's has two?"

The children roared with laughter.

"But it has, Teacher, it has only got one side, Teacher, and I did what you told me and filled it up with numbers, Teacher."

"Bring it here, bring it here," said the teacher.

When he saw it the teacher was very cross, complained that the boy was a nasty, cocky, tricky, little boy and that he would come to no good. In fact the nasty boy was one of those elitist, gifted children and he was right, his piece was the same as all the others except that he had fixed it so that it had only one side. How can this be explained?

See Answer No. 97.

T.15   You Will Obey

I have had an inordinate number of nieces and nephews and my position as favourite uncle is seriously undermined by an unpleasant and disturbing trick which I play upon each as they reach the suitable age.

"I shall give you a command which you will be forced to obey", I say. Enthusiastic and vehement denials.

"If you stand on that stool and I order you to get down, you will certainly do it." The innocent child cannot get on to the stool fast enough.

"Get down from that stool."

"No, Uncle, I won't. I won't get down."

It is at this point that the fiendish smile spreads over my wicked face. "You will, you know," I say, and walk away, sit down and start reading a book.

I have had an unhappy nephew, stuck there on the stool for half-an-hour, begging me to forbid him to get down from it. But he who makes fools of innocent children is asking for revenge and it is for the reader to solve the problem of how my unkindness was finally punished. I shall begin the story, it is for you to end it.

Having been caught in their turn, two nieces and a nephew counter-attacked as follows:

They arranged three stools at the corners of an equilateral

triangle. There were nearby two sets of stilts, which were 4ft 6ins high, within reach of one of the stools but they were not long enough to bridge the distance between the stools.

Leaping up on to the stools the children defied me to order them to get down. I gave my orders peremptorily. "Get down from that stool, Michael. Get down from that stool, Debbie. Get down from that stool, Barbara."

"Will you give us a quid each if we all disobey you?"

"I must not encourage disobedience but you cannot disobey me, so I can safely promise to do so."

A minute later I was surrounded by joyous, dancing, jumping children as I dolefully handed out the money, which their intelligence had earned.

Your problem, reader, is to say how they did it? None of the children could walk on stilts.

See Answer No. 99.

T.16   Pouring Puttonos

Many jokes, tastelessly, deal with stupidity. In Mensa we avoid racialism by writing jokes about those we call Densans but the reader can identify their own target for this joke. If they are English, it is an Irishman; if they are Irish, it is a Kerry man; if the reader is American, the target is a Pole; if he is Swedish, it is a Finn; if an Armenian, a Georgian; and if Chinese, any foreigner.

The person of this unsettled nationality went to the pub next door to get a quart of ale for his master, the farmer. Having forgotten to bring a jug, he asked the landlord to pour the ale into his trilby hat. But some of the quart was left over, so, with a brilliant stroke of insight, he turned the hat upside down and invited the potman to put the rest in the dimple in the top. He rushed home with his ale and offered it to the farmer in the dimple full of ale.

"That's not a quart", roared the farmer, "where's the rest of it?"

The grinning Kerry/Irish/Polish/Densan/Georgian/Foreigner smilingly turned the hat upside down again, saying, "there it is."

Knowing the deep, penetrating, awe-inspiring intelligence of my readers, I know that many of them will have seen, by now, how the quart of beer might have been safely brought home, with the beer carried in the hat and the dent as described. There is no catch. He carries the hat, it is full of beer and so is the dent which, as a container, is upside down.

Question A: There is a way to do it, what is it?

See Answer No. 13.

But the problem I am working up to is the awe-inspiring difficult problem of the Hungarian Baron who was greatly displeased with the Court Jester whose jokes had been cutting too near the bone. "For your impudence", said the evil Count, "you shall receive a thousand lashes."

"Come on, Baron", said the Fool, foolishly, "be a sport, give me a chance."

The Baron would rather have been accused of genocide than of being unsportsmanlike so he set the fool a problem. If he solved it, he would get off with 500 lashes.

Question B: "Here is a puncheon of my finest Tokay," he said, "and here are two wine mugs. This one holds 5 puttonos and this one holds 3 puttonos. You are not allowed to mark the mugs in any way and you have to contrive to get exactly 1 puttono, neither more nor less, into each mug, touching nothing but the barrel and the two mugs and, of course, as a special favour, the floor with your feet."

I need hardly say that the fool solved the problem or I would not be telling the story. In solving it, he created great distress in the Baron and if it were not for the fact that everyone got very drunk during the exercise, he might have been severely punished. But in the morning, memories were so hazy that the whole incident was forgotten. Indeed everyone forgot how the problem was solved. So my demand that the solver should take on this horrible problem is especially unjust.

See Answer No. 19.

T.17 That Crafty Land-Grabber, Ali

A wily Eastern potentate having lived a long life and enjoyed procreative games and sports in a large harem, had many sons and innumerable daughters. The elitist autocrat wanted to make sure that his wealth and power should be inherited by one with the intelligence to administer it well, and never having heard of Germaine Greer, decided to leave it to the most crafty of his many, many sons. He composed a puzzle which tested the boys not only for intelligence but also for what was to him the supreme virtue, acquisitiveness for land.

A large, true ellipse was drawn on the desert sand and his many sons were invited, each of them, to mark three points on the perimeter. The son whose three points defined the largest triangle in area was to inherit.

The sons went to work eagerly, racing round on Arab steeds, and most thrust three lances beflagged as labels into the perimeter of the elipse at various points. Soon there were hundreds of spears and flags and enormous confusion. Ali Ben Yusef, an undersized, unpopular lad, who picked his nose and hated riding camels, after some serious measuring and marking in the night, banged in three tent pegs which turned out to contain the triangle of largest area.
Question A: Was the triangle equilateral?

See Answer No. 89.

Question B: How did he find the corners of the triangle?

See Answer No. 93.

T.18 Making Things More Difficult

The satisfaction gained from solving a problem increases with the initial difficulty. And what gives the strongest impression of difficulty is often a puzzle where the information given appears to be insufficient or misleading.

My father once asked me, "What is it? It's green, it hangs in a cage and it squeaks." I tried all the obvious answers and then gave up. "What is it?" I said.

"A red herring", said my father.

My childish voice went up to a piping, aggrieved treble. "But it's not green."

"This one was painted green."

"But it doesn't hang in a cage."

"There's nothing to stop you hanging a red herring in a cage."

"But, Dad, it doesn't squeak."

"I put that in to make it harder."

Artfully, he waited a week or two before he asked me the next one. "It has four legs, feathers and a brick in the middle." But I had been immunised by the first experience.

"I don't know, I give up."

"A feather bed."

"I know, you put the brick in the middle to make it harder." So you see where I got it from. Which brings us to the next problem. So can you do this one?

It has four legs and flies. What is it?

See Answer No. 78.

T.19   Nine Digits Squared Away

A Victorian father with an authoritarian disposition paraded his nine children to instruct them in arithmetic. He had bought up some numbered running singlets, one with each of the nine digits upon it. The children were instructed to don the singlets and parade before their stern, side-whiskered pipe-smoking father.

"Now children, form into four groups so as to make up four numbers."

After much shuffling about, the children finally stood in four groups thus:

21   47   596   38

"No! no! no! Wrong! Wrong! None of those numbers are square numbers."

The oldest child spoke: "But you did not tell us that they should be square numbers, Papa."

"Do I have to tell you everything? I left that information out so as to make it a real test of intelligence. Now then, children, quickly re-arrange yourselves so as to make four numbers, each of them must be a square number, the square of an integer."

At this point we ask the reader to come in and take over the children's difficult problem.

Question A: Can the children meet this difficult condition and form four groups so that each represents a square number? If so, what are the four square numbers?

See Answer No. 58.

Question B: Can the children do it in only three groups?

See Answer No. 68.

Question C: And suppose the children had to stand all in one group, can it be done then? If it can, what is the smallest square number that can be formed from all the digits and what is the largest?

See Answer No. 73.

T.20   Getting Things Mixed Up

The sentence below might be called Mairshops and maybe the discerning reader will infuriate me by seeing why.

The list of words below are in disorder. When they have been put back into order they should come together to form a new aphorism. It is your difficult task to order them.

A: bends dogma science breaks
B: prejudice judgment condemn pardon
C: unlike minds think great

D: compassion discrimination discrimination compassion is all is but not all
E: without one clapping discernment is handed praise
F: performance praise condemnation improves excuses improves
G: is intelligence bewilderment without freedom
H: malice dagger of sharp the a has handle
I: doing thing their poor everybody produces own a of lot things
J: statement not to it to a is not is that show disinterested that is show false

See Answer No. 52.

T.21   Turning the Golden Cone

Bricks, tea, iron ingots, cowrie shells, axe heads, arrowheads, and little pieces of paper. All these at one time and another have served as money.

But in the obscure banana republic, Euphoria, which is rich in gold and poor in civilisation, the usual form of money is large ingots which, disguised, would pass out without suspicion. He because this is the kind of mould they find easy to dig in the sand and partly because of the law which is strictly enforced that he who is caught taking gold out of the country shall be punished by being forced to sit on it for many hours. Those that survive this painful if sedentary experience show almost an aversion for the metal thereafter.

Now the Euphorian ingot is substantial, it weighs 20 kilograms so that despite this wicked practice many try to think up ways to overcome this problem. One of these was an Austrian turner employed to work the one lathe in the country. Having earned a good deal at his trade and wanting to take it from the country, he hit upon the idea of putting one of these cones on to his lathe and turning it to the shape of a cylinder, the normal shape for iron ingots which, disguised, would pass out without suspicion. He figured that even if he were caught his punishment would be less savage.

But he was in a quandary. He could make a long thin cylinder a good proportion of the length of the cone or he could make a short fat cylinder. Which would give him the greatest quantity of gold? In the end, being no mathematician, he made a rough guess and cut the cone in half and turned that into the cylinder with the widest diameter that he could.

What proportion of the weight of gold he might have got did he actually get?

See Answer No. 1.

T.22 Are Squearths Really All Nuphs?

All educated people now realise that pprills, squearths and glops have all been proved to be simply forms of nuph. It is also well established that squearths are both glops *and* nuphs. However, there is a complication. Recent work has established that there are glops which are neither squearths, gdynxs nor pprills. Further, there are squearths which are neither gdynxs nor yet pprills.

Admittedly some pprills *are* glops as are all squearths and even some gdynxs as well. Now that we know more about gdynxs, that some are squearths, some glops and some, unfortunately, both pprills *and* squearths, there are certain urgent questions that can be answered definitively.

1. Can the universe contain such an unfortunate creature that, to be truthful, it must admit that it is a pprill, a nuph, a squearth, a glop and also a gdynx?
2. Consider those gdynxs which are not nuphs, can they possibly be glops?
3. If a pprill is a squearth, is it also a glop and can it possibly be a gdynx?

See Answer No. 41.

T.23 The Square on the Diagonal

Draw a square as given below. Now make one of the sides of the square the diagonal of a second square. These are the first two terms of an infinite series: you can now make the side of the second square the diagonal of a third square. There are obviously many ways to calculate the relative breadth of two squares, a known number of steps apart along this series, but what is the kickself* simple way.

Question: If the first square is a square metre, what is the length of the side of the eleventh square in the series? What is the simple rule for determining the size?

See Answer No. 7.

Note: * See Chapter 5.

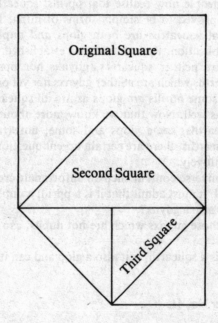

Original Square

Second Square

Third Square

T.24 The Golden Ball and the Oxford Professors

An Oxford Professor named Hall
Possessed an Octagonal Ball,
The Square of its Weight
Divided by Eight
Was π times the Root of Sod All.

Now the more perceptive reader will have spotted immediately the logical and mathematical flaws in the above statement. If it was octagonal, it can hardly have been a ball, and the mathematics seems to contain serious flaws. I am now in a position to reveal the true story. The ball *was* in fact a ball, not octagonal, and made of pure gold. Together with another Professor he had obtained it in an illicit fashion during an archaeological dig in Peru. The two accomplices being born complexifiers, fell into a dispute about how they should divide up this valuable object.

One had a fancy to have a solid gold paperweight and as a ball is not much use for that purpose, decided that it must be a cylinder; so he said, "All I want is a cylinder from the ball and I can turn this up on the lathe in the laboratory. All the rest of it, the golden swarf, you shall have and you can sell it for a considerable sum."

The second professor did some calculations and proved to his own satisfaction that any true cylinder turned from the sphere must contain less than half the volume of the sphere and so he agreed to the terms.

Was he wise? If the total weight of gold in the ball was 1 kilogram, what was the least weight of swarf his friend could make in turning a true cylinder from the golden ball?

See Answer No. 28.

T.25 Slow Burn or Shooting

The evil dictator of a rotten banana republic had found out one of his lieutenants in a lie. The punishment was to be death.

"I will teach you not to lie," said the evil but, it seems, illogical ruler. "Your last words shall be one sentence. It shall be a sentence that can be either a truth or a lie. If you tell the truth, you shall be shot. If you tell a lie, you will die for days over the small fire."

The prisoner's reply caused so much confusion and delay that he got away with his life, though others died. Guess what his reply was.

See Answer No. 21.

T.26 Escherism

At one stage of my career I was a factory manager and the first version of a drawing of the well-known Escheristic triangle with illogical joints came into my hands.

Mischievously, I got one of my draughtsmen to make it up as a normal machine drawing and then sent for a foreman and told him, in a business-like way, to get out half-a-dozen samples in a hurry for a client who might place a big order. Nothing happened for three days except that the foreman concerned was even more curt and grumpy than usual. On the third day he came into my office to talk to me about some other job, dropped the drawing on my desk and departed without a further word.

The artist, Escher, has made many such illogical drawings. But to the matter in hand. Readers with the slightest knowledge of industry will immediately recognise that this high speed, low rigidity, double sprung, low inertia, high torque, twelve gate, valve fortified, high vibration ratio, Tulse Hill-type internally fired scrorlp has been sabotaged before it got off the drawing-board by a follower of Escher.

He has inserted a fiendishly clever error into this drawing which caused months of disruption on the production line, 17 strikes and finally led to the shutdown of the factory.

The solver is given the impossible task of discovering the error that had been insidiously slipped into the design. Give the co-ordinates of the area where the error is to be found.

See Answer No. 15.

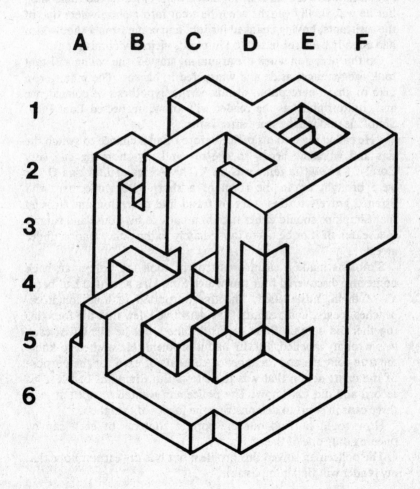

T.27 Simpkin's Come-Uppance

There will be deep rejoicing in the reader's heart when he learns how Simpkins was finally brought to book and justice done. Simpkins was the evil practical joker who switched labels on tinned fruit and then won bets about their content in grocer's shops. See Puzzle No. T.5 "The Evil Ways of Augustus Henry Simpkins". Simpkins was very careful; he never went twice to the same shop but he was finally caught when he went into a shop where one of the assistants, having changed his job, had come from a shop which had already been subjected to Simpkin's vicious victimisations.

On this occasion when the argument started, the young assistant took the manager aside and whispered in his ear. The manager, a man of sharp perception, dismissed the hypothesis of coincidence and, quite rightly as the reader will know, suspected Foul Play. Simpkins told me the story afterwards.

"He called me into his office before I had a chance to switch the tins and when he began to eye me and my shopping bag very closely, I knew the game was up." The Forces of Law and Order were brought in, in the form of a sharp-eyed policeman who listened gravely to this story of fraud and deception and insisted that Simpkins should either take him back to his house and submit to a search of it or be taken immediately to the police station under arrest.

Simpkins made a clean breast of it, took the policeman back home and discovered four tins which Simpkins admitted had been, all of them, mislabelled. The tins purported to hold tomatoes, peaches, pears, and peanuts. The detective knew that the four tins together did contain these four substances but he knew that each was wrongly labelled. But he had a problem. He wanted to know the true contents and the labelled contents of each for the purpose of the court action that was to follow. But Simpkins had lost his record and did not know. The policeman wanted to open at least three cans in court to demonstrate the falsity of the labels.

How could he find out the correct contents of each can by opening only one of them?

The policeman solved this problem but it is my earnest hope that my reader will find it impossible.

See Answer No. 38.

Starting Something You Cannot Finish

All progress is precarious, and the solution of one problem brings us face to face with another problem.

Martin Luther King, Jr., *Strength to Love*

Serious Words About Series

The curtains opened and a man announced, "Is there a Doctor in the House, a man has collapsed."

"I'm a doctor." A beautiful young lady with Loren figure in low-cut evening dress hurried forward.

The patient, a lusty stage-hand, came round to find a disturbing vision with the lovely creature leaning solicitously over him.

"Let me see your throat — say, ninety-nine."

Perhaps the young man was simply confused. He began reciting very slowly, "One. . .two. . .three. . .".

That stage-hand was creating a series; [1, 2. . .99]. The numbers 1 to 99, and those beyond, come to that, are the simplest example of a series. It is the series which starts with nothing and which is subjected to the operator "add 1" and then set to "run" as computer programmers say. Other obvious series are: 2, 4, 6, 8, 10 and 1, 4, 9, 16, 25. . .

What is a series? There must be elements which must be arranged or be arrangeable in a linear fashion. They must be invariant in some way, i.e. the elements must all be one type of thing, numbers, letters, symbols. But in another way they must exhibit variance. The main point is that the variant aspect of each element must depend in some way on those that go before (and therefore, of course, with those that come after). A line of integers where there is *no* relationship between successive numbers is called a *random series*, a contradiction! But the muddling thing is that for any given random series it is possible, if you look hard enough, to *find* a rule which justifies it and worse, if you like, an infinite number of sets of rules of increasing complexity.

There are two ways of making series into problems, one is simply to give a few terms in the series and ask the solver to give the next term. The other method is to construct a logical series and then to make a deliberate error which the solver has to correct.

The essence is a starting point and a transform operation based on some logical relationship and thus the system is set up to produce what is usually an infinite number of successive transforms.

A normal series problem could be called a monological problem in that the relationship is along a linear dimension, each term being associated with its neighbour on a line. But we can extend a series in another dimension into a matrix or array. This can have what could be called a bi-logical scheme, like a crossword, it can make sense in both directions. This type is, for obvious reasons, other things being equal, harder to compose and easier to solve. A crossword puzzle, a magic square, or one of the items from the intelligence test Raven's Progressive Matrices, are examples of bi-logical arrays.

Tri-logical forms are equally possible but I cannot remember having seen any. Here the scheme is extended to the third dimension and the three-dimensional form makes sense in three directions. These are yet again, other things equal, even harder to compose and even easier to solve but by way of novelty I give a few examples of tri-logicals; here every term in a three-dimensional array has to be in correct relationship with its neighbours in all three dimensions, down, across and through, as it were.

In the following numerical puzzles you are asked to designate the missing term, either from the alternatives offered or from your inner consciousness.

A Series of Ten Troublesome Teasers

S.1 2, 3, 4, 6, 8, 12, 14, 18, 20, ?

See Answer No. 2.

S.2 3, 6, 13, 26, 33, 66, ?

See Answer No. 8.

S.3 9, 10, 12, 14, 15, 16, 18, 20, 21, 22, 24, 25, 26, 27, 28, ?

See Answer No. 14.

S.4 22, 20, 10, 8, 4, 2, ?

See Answer No. 20.

S.5 4, 8, 32, 512, ?

See Answer No. 26.

S.6 364, 361, 19, 16, 4, 1, ?

See Answer No. 33.

S.7   5 ⅕ , 4¼, 3⅓, 2½, ?

See Answer No. 39.

S.8   1, 1, 2, 2, 4, 2, 4, 2, 4, 6, 2, 6, 4, 2, 4, 6, ?, ?, ?

See Answer No. 45.

S.9   15, 15, 13, 13, 13, 14, ?

See Answer No. 50.

S.10   1, 0.5, 0.3333, 0.2, 0.1429, 0.0909, 0.0769, ?

See Answer No. 56.

53

Diagram Series

Series, of course, need not concern numbers. Letters, diagrams, can form a logical series.

There follows a number of series where the solver is asked to select from the lettered figures that which fits most appropriately where the question mark is.

S.11   I Hope This Upsets You

These shapes are all different but there is a principle lying behind their arrangement. Which of the lettered shapes in the line below logically goes where the question mark is?

See Answer No. 61.

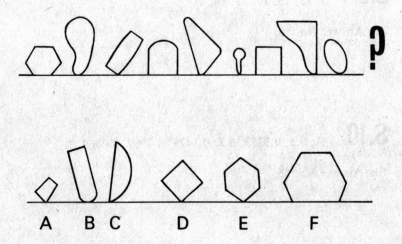

54

S.12 Concentrate!

A. There is a common underlying principle which connects this succession of concentric diagrams. Your task is to select the lettered diagram below which best fits the position where the question mark is.

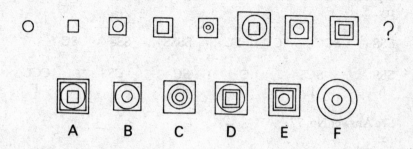

See Answer No. 66.

B. What is the meaning, expressed in other terms, of the designated diagram?

See Answer No. 81.

S.13 What Next?

There is a system behind the arrangement of the letters below. Which of the letters in the second line should logically take the place of the question mark?

Y   P   I   D   ?

T   Z   Q   A   L   M

See Answer No. 72.

S.14 A Series of Curved Letters to Straighten Out

This odd assembly of letters hides a meaningful series. One, and only one, of the lettered series below belongs where the question mark is. You have no real chance of guessing but you might as well try.

SSS   SCC   C   SC   SSSS   SSS   SC   ?

SSS	SCS	C	SC	CSS	CCC
A	B	C	D	E	F

See Answer No. 77.

S.15 Random Squiggles

Here is a line of what appear to be random squiggles. The human mind is built to search for order. Sometimes it finds order that is not really there. Is there any order in this array? If so, what is it and which, if any, of the lettered squiggles should logically be put where the question mark is?

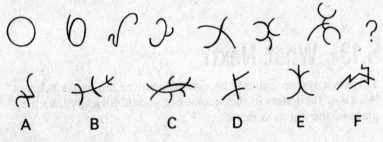

A   B   C   D   E   F

See Answer No. 82.

S.16   Cut That Out!

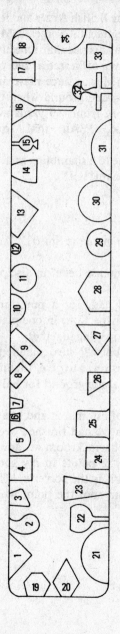

A man had a large oblong piece of plywood and he had to cut from it for a jigsaw a number of patterns, each of which had at least one straight edge. The man was not very intelligent but he was obsessively systematic. He tried to utilize the straight edges of the piece of plywood and so arranged them all round the edge, as shown. Having an exaggerated idea of order, he also arranged them, despite their many differences, in a systematic order but, being distracted, he greatly irritated himself by making a mistake.

Can you find the two neighbouring patterns which broke the unnecessary rule he had imposed upon himself?

See Answer No. 86.

S.17 The Martinet

I was once the least soldierly sergeant in the British Army and it was my fate to get into a regiment whose Regimental Sergeant Major was known as "Tiger" Jackson because of his peculiar ferocity on parade. His roar was reputed to bring leaves off a tree at 200 yards in summer and 400 yards in the autumn. I was once marching a squad of wireless operators across the parade ground when there were 20 squads around and Tiger Jackson, from 150 yards away, roared the ear-drum splitting phrase, "'Alt that squad, Sarjeareeeaant."

I gave the command and the squad came to a shambling halt.

"Wheaaarts your na-a-ame, Sarjeareeeaant?!!!!"

"Sar'nt Serebriakoff, Sah!"

"Wha-a-a-at!"

"Sar'nt Serebriakoff, Sah!"

"From now on, in this regiment, your name is Smiff!" And it was.

Yes, Jackson was a martinet with an intense belief in discipline, regularity, order and correct procedure.

On another occasion after my squad had, for a punishment, swept the parade ground, he found, on inspection, in one place, a cigarette end, a dead match and a bottle top lying together.

"What's this great heap of festering rubbish?" he demanded and giving me strict instructions, on the orders I was to give, told me to march my offending squad around the parade ground for half-an-hour.

The diagram below indicates the path of our march and I have to tell you that I was in more trouble when we had finished because Tiger Jackson had been watching from a barrackroom window and had noted my error. I have numbered the points in my squad's route where I ordered them to turn and it is the solver's difficult task to be as sharp-eyed as the Tiger and spot the point where I made the mistake.

Where did the squad go wrong?

See Answer No. 90.

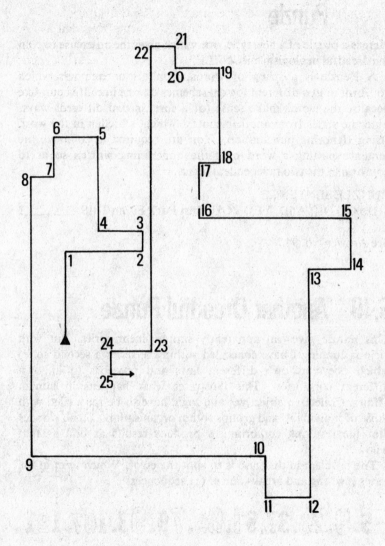

S.18 An Unforgivably Difficult Punzle

Here is a puzzle of a new type, one which gives me an excuse to coin the dreadful neologism "PUNZLE".

A Punzle is a string of words, symbols or numbers which conform to two different logical schemes on one line. It is pun-like because the words make sense (of a sort) in two different ways. Find the series from another context which is hidden in the word string (ignoring punctuation). You are required to complete the sentence putting a word over the underlining written so as to conform to the two independent logics.

PUNZLE SENTENCE
I Do GO Off; AnD, YEs! YOU Must ParT FrOm ThIS _____?

See Answer No. 94.

S.19 Another Dreadful Punzle

This punzle gives an apparently simple linear series. But with vicious cunning I have concealed within the series a second series which obeys its own different laws and proceeds to its own different conclusion. This illustrates what happens in human affairs. Collective objectives and logic have to be reconciled with those of individuals and groups within organisations. Small wonder that the resulting compromises produce results as odd as that below:

The problem in this case is to spot the error. Which term in the series is wrong and breaks one of the sequences?

$$-5. \; 9. \; 23. \; 37. \; 51. \; 65. \; 79. \; 93. \; 107. \; 121.$$

See Answer No. 85.

And here are examples of bi-logical arrays, like a crossword puzzle, the array has to make logical sense in two dimensions.

S.20 Senseless Shapes and Scattered Letters

This is a bi-logical array, the logic being well hidden and muddled with irrelevance. Which of the lettered squares fits where the question mark is?

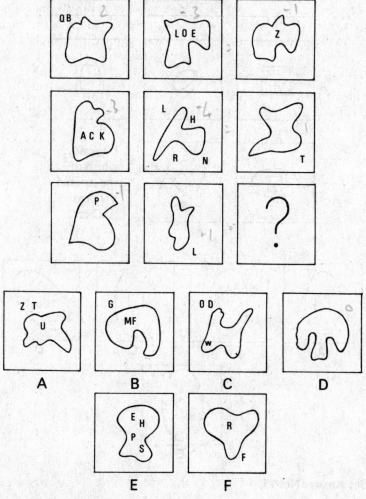

See Answer No. 80.

S.21 Ellipses and Squares

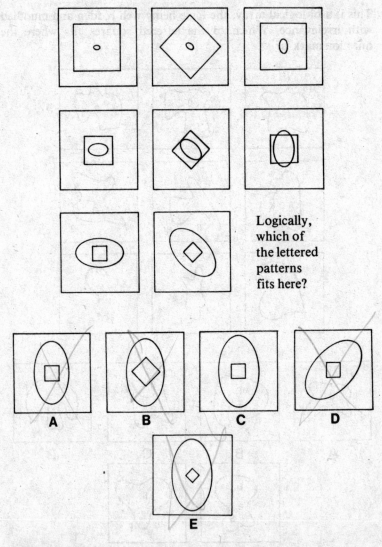

Logically, which of the lettered patterns fits here?

A   B   C   D

E

See Answer No. 75.

S.22 Brzöibian Magic Square

One never knows what features of one culture will interest another. When Brzöibs reached Earth they went mad about Magic Squares. An example of their version is given below. Their Magic Square, like ours, adds to the same number down, across or diagonally. Knowing that a Brzöib has seven manipulopods, what is their Magic Square in human symbols?

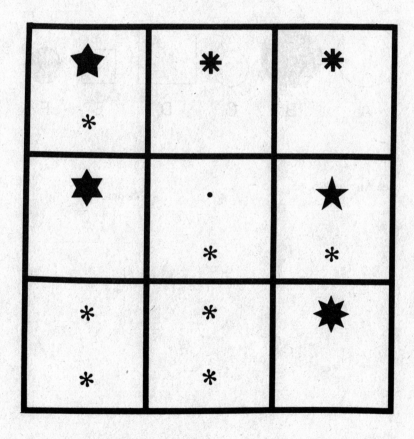

See Answer No. 96.

S.23   Cube of Cubes

And here is an example of a tri-logical 3D array. There are principles of transformation operating in three dimensions, one of the cubes on the cube of cubes shown is out of sight behind the others. Which, logically, of the lettered patterns shown below should appear on the faces of that cube?

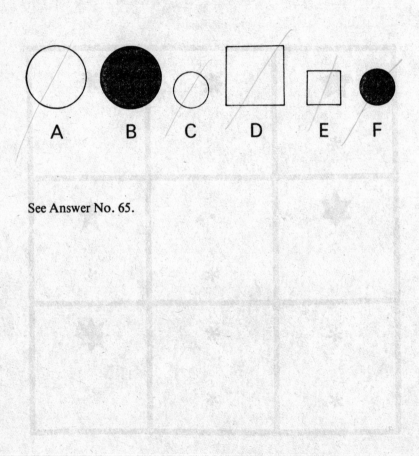

See Answer No. 65.

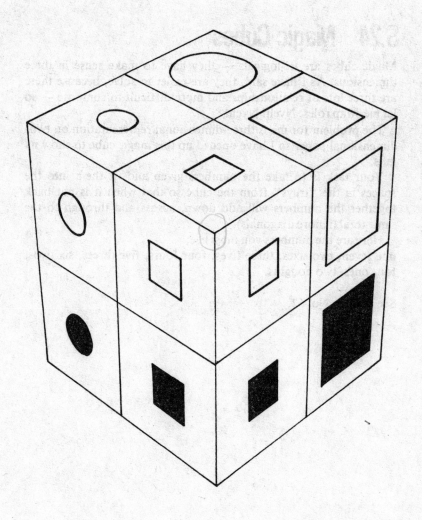

S.24 Magic Cubes

Magic cubes are tri-logicals — they have to make sense in three dimensions. As I have said, they are easier to solve, because there are three lots of relationships and more difficult to compose — so let me swap roles. Nyeh! Nyeh!

The problem for me is three-dimensional representation on two-dimensional paper so I have opened up this magic cube to show its guts.

Your task is to take the numbers given and fit them into the spaces in the "trays" from the cube so that when it is put back together the numbers will add down, across and through to the same total (ignore diagonals).

Here are the numbers you must use:
one seven, two sixes, three fives, four fours, five threes, six twos, four ones, two noughts.

See Answer No. 62.

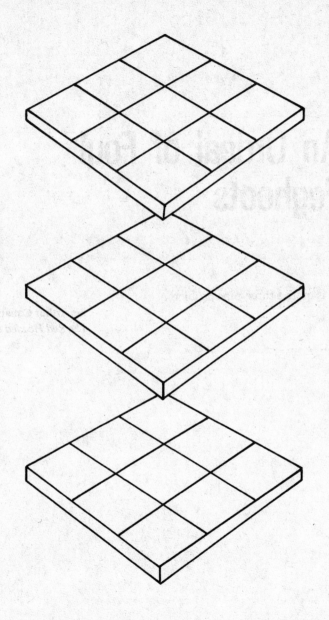

An Ordeal of Foul Feghoots

It is quite a three-pipe problem.

Sir Arthur Conan Doyle
The Red Headed League

Feghoot Puzzles

"What the — expletive — blasphemy — indelicacy" you will be asking, "is a Feghoot?" And well you may. A Mensa member from Kentucky, a certain Mr. Harper Fowley, who edits a Mensa Journal for members in remote places called *The Isolated M* (*M* is Mensan for Mensan), is responsible for the evil plague, Feghootitis which infects Mensa. A character who, but for Harper, would have remained mercifully obscure called Feghoot, in a lost science fiction story used to compose these "whole sentence" puns, and Harper Fowley spread the plague.

A familiar catch-phrase, saying or aphorism is interpreted like a pun according to a different sense associated with the sound, to mean something entirely different. Some distortion is allowed to help the evil business forward. The task is to tell a tale which leads up to the required sentence.

I have turned these distorted examples of literary trivialisation into a puzzle in this way — *I* tell the lead up tale and *you* find the distorted catch-phrase which makes pun-like sense of the tale.

A sickening example of a Feghoot follows — after that, over to you.

The Squire's Outing

The West Mudshire Lords of the Manor Club arranged an outing to the zoo. Only three attended, Squire George, Squire Harry and Squire F.G. They, naturally, had to go for a ride on the animals. George went on a giraffe, Harry on a camel but there was a problem with Squire F.G. (or Fat Guts) because he weighed as much as the other two together and so had to ride on a hippopotamus. And all this proves, are you ready, that the "squire on the hippopotamus is equal to the sum of the squires on the other two rides". Yuck!

So now — solve these nauseating Feghoots — and become infected!

Feghoot Answers:
For those sad solvers who *still* cannot fathom the *original* phrase, they are listed on page 147 after the answers.

F.1   The Professor's Table-Cloth

The Professor was very proud of a velvet table-cloth which had been given after twenty years service at the University. He complained to his wife about her habit of putting the great heaps of books from his desk on the table when she dusted the former.

"One or two books won't crush the nap," he said, "but

_____ _____ _____ _____ _____ _____"

Fill in the six words which form a slightly distorted version of a popular saying.

See Answer No. 3.

70

F.2 Muddled Hearses

A murderer took his girl friend to the funeral of his victim so as to impress her. They watched the hearse arrive and listened to the lamentations of the relatives and their complaints against the police who had not traced the murderer. When they had all gone, the couple triumphantly inspected the gravestone, only to find that the name on it was not that of the murderer's victim.

"We followed the wrong funeral," said the disappointed assassin.

"Yes," said his sweetheart, "evidently that was . . .

_____ _____ _____ _____ _____"

See Answer No. 9.

F.3 The Running Dogs

An anthropologist aimed to study a small remote settlement in Africa. The Chief provided splendid hospitality and asked him what more he could do to help.

"I am surprised and pleased to find that you have electric light in this village but I noticed that in the evenings when I am writing up my notes the lights go dim and I cannot see to write."

"I put this right," said the Chief, "I put this right, I get more dogs."

"Dogs?"

"Yes, baas, we got no engine, baas. We got dogs on treadmill make light. Two dogs no good, no light, but . . .

_____ _____ _____ _____ _____"

See Answer No. 16.

F.4 Cattle Call

This one might be too difficult, the distortion is positively fiendish.

A Cockney, his friend Pat, the Irishman, and Dougal, a Scot, all went for a holiday on Pat's farm in Donegal where the Scot and the Cockney slept in a tent on the field. They were awakened at six in the morning when Pat, who was already in the fields, and near the tent, called out in a loud voice to his cowherd who was just trudging to work. The noise woke the couple and Dougal asked what it was all about. The Cockney put his head out of the door, saw what had happened, and said, "T'was only tha' . . .

_____ _____ _____ _____ _____"

See Answer No. 22.

F.5 Sawing Trays

A cabinet maker was instructed to prepare the timber for a thousand wooden trays. He had to saw some birch fillet for the rim but found that the circular saw had a burnt-out motor.

Naturally, he went to the foreman and said, "The circular saw is broken down and I . . .

_____ _____ _____ _____ _____ _____ _____"

See Answer No. 27.

F.6 Red Mouth

The dentist, Alfred Bott, was curious about his Singhalese customer whose teeth crevices were full of a gooey substance which was normal except for its bright red colour.

"It comes from chewing the betel nut," explained his customer.

Mr. Bott cleaned the client's teeth and this was an obvious case of the . . .

"_____ _____ _____ _____ _____"

See Answer No. 35.

F.7 Darwin's Gin

Darwin, though he lived to an advanced age, was a very shy man and unlike his friend and champion, Huxley, he hated giving speeches. In fact he fell into the habit of drinking a long quick gin before he delivered each lecture. He called the drink he took each time . . .

"_____ _____ _____ _____ _____ _____"

See Answer No. 40.

I Could Have Kicked Myself

Problems worthy of attack prove their worth by hitting back.

Piet Hein, *Problems*, Crooks, 1966

I Could Have Kicked Myself

This is the heading of a series of puzzles which at the time of writing I am running in the British Mensa Newsletter.

Kickself posers started during a conversation with Clive Sinclair and Arthur C. Clarke. A kickself poser is one where the answer is impossible before, but obvious after you know it. When you hear the answer you feel like kicking yourself for not seeing it immediately.

Quite a number of the puzzles in this book, I am delighted to say, are likely to leave you with your ankles black and blue with self-mortification when you read the answer. They prove that high intelligence is no defence against stupidity and that intelligence is a necessary but not a sufficient condition of excellence.

K.1 Time to Strike

If it takes a clock two seconds to strike two o'clock, how long will it take to strike three o'clock?

See Answer No. 4.

K.2 The Jilted Witch

In a mountain village in Switzerland one winter a couple were being married. During the wedding a girl, jilted by the bridegroom, appeared and made a scene.

"The wedding bell will not ring," she said and immediately took poison and was rushed to hospital.

Sure enough when the bell-ringer tried, there was no sound from the bell. Some said she was a witch and had cast a spell but others thought she had tied the clapper. After the ceremony they went to the belfry but found everything in working order. There were no signs of anything that would prevent the bell from ringing. How had she stopped the bell ringing but left no trace?

See Answer No. 10.

K.3 Hurried Barbers

Three customers in a barber's shop each need a haircut and a shave. There are two barbers working and they both work at the same speed. Each takes a quarter of an hour for a haircut and five minutes for a shave. They are both in a hurry to be off, how quickly can they finish the work?

See Answer No. 17.

K.4   Blind Man's Socks

A blind man has 51 socks in a drawer, 17 red, 17 blue and 17 green.

Question A: How many socks must he take out so that he is sure of having a pair of socks of each colour?

See Answer No. 23.

Question B: And how many will he need to get a pair of any colour?

See Answer No. 30.

K.5   Cuts and Ends

I have an object in my hand which is a thread-like length of material. I cut clean through it with a pair of scissors. I have not created two pieces with four ends but only one piece with two ends. What is the object?

See Answer No. 36.

K.6 As Easy As Pie

Puzzle setters love series because they are easy to compose and difficult to solve. You can, as I have suggested, select any series of numbers at random and with sufficient ingenuity, work out a relationship between them but the relationship *required* is the simplest, that which, retrospectively at least, is most obvious.

Take this series

$$3 \quad 1 \quad 4 \quad 1 \quad 5 \quad ?$$

Easy? Wait! You are invited to give the *second* most obvious answer. Give the integer which goes at the end of this series, where the question mark is.

See Answer No. 42.

K.7 "Head South Pardner"

When they were there, the tramlines on the long straight road from Leeds to Headingley went many miles through drear suburbs. One gloomy wet night, as the last tram bumped and rattled along the dim gas-lit road, it slowed a little its stately pace because a lone, wet, drunken citizen was stumbling towards Headingley in the middle of the track. Taking pity on the drenched walker, the driver shouted "Headingley?"

"Keep shtraight on, you can't miss it."

But this is the problem. A man walks exactly due south for exactly three miles and then he walks due north for two miles. What is the maximum distance he can be from his starting point?

See Answer No. 47.

K.8 The Racist Ice Cream Vendor

The little boy came running back to home, crying, "All my school friends can buy ice cream but the man won't sell it to me."

"Why not?" his father asked.

"He says he won't sell me ice cream because I am a Jewish boy."

The father's indignation can be imagined. "Come with me, son," he said grimly.

The ice cream man was doing a roaring trade. "Is it true you won't sell my son ice cream because he is Jewish?"

"I won't sell my ice cream to a Jewish boy."

"That's anti-Semitism. You're a racist. It's illegal."

The vendor shrugged and spread his hands wide in an expressive gesture. "So how can I be an anti-Semite when I'm a Jew myself?"

"You'll sell my son ice cream or I'll complain to the Race Relations Board."

"No Jewish child shall eat my ice cream!"

"Right. Come on, son, we'll go and see the police."

"Wait, wait!" The ice cream vendor beckoned to the enraged father and taking him by the arm, whispered something in his ear. The father walked off briskly with his son, and when he was out of sight, he explained.

"So you see, my son, it seems quite reasonable after all that he wouldn't want to sell his ice cream to a Jewish boy."

"I quite understand, Daddy, I think he was right to discriminate."

The puzzle is what caused the sudden change in attitude of the parent? How did he reconcile his son to the discrimination?

See Answer No. 51.

K.9 I'll Show You My Operation, I'll Show You My Figure

The judge stopped the case to question the witness himself. "You must try to help the Court, young lady. You say that this man pestered you yet you tell us that you go out with him every night and go away for weekends with him, staying in one room as man and wife? Does this not sound like a regular liaison?"

"It was, your Honour, regular as anything, pester, pester, pester, pester."

Which brings me to the sometimes odd effects of doing things over and over again, in mathematics.

I have chosen an integer (whole number) and a mathematical operation which I may perform upon it. I perform the operation on the integer and then upon the result and then upon the result of that. In this way I perform the operation eight times. As a result of this chain of operations I finish with the same number with which I started. I now perform the operation once more. The result is a quantity, one millionth as great as the original number.

Can you select an integer and a mathematical operation which produce these results?

See Answer No. 53.

K.10 Gun Switch

The Counsel for the Prosecution was in good form. He felt he had the accused on the run. The charge was espionage and the suspect was under cross-examination.

"You have told the Court," said the Counsel for the Prosecution, "that you put the gun in your pocket and you have sworn that you did not touch this loaded weapon from the time you put it there until the moment that you were arrested. You will remember that I questioned you very closely as to which pocket you put the gun in, and you told us that it was in your overcoat, the outside pocket on the right side. The Court will remember, and I have it here very clearly in my notes, that the police evidence (evidence which the Defence in no way challenges), is that the gun was found on the left-hand *inner* pocket of your overcoat. My question to you is this. How did the gun get from the *outside right* side of your overcoat to the inside *left side* of it if, as you tell us, neither you nor anyone else touched it from the moment you put it there till the moment you were arrested?''

At this point the Prosecuting Counsel began to be uneasy because he noticed a smile of triumph on the face of the Counsel for the Defence. It was justified; the prisoner produced a perfectly sensible, logical and fully acceptable answer. He showed how the gun could be found in the left-hand inner pocket without having been moved from the right-hand outer pocket. The pockets were perfectly normal ones and there was no connection between any of the four pockets in the coat.

See Answer No. 57.

K.11   The Ups and Downs of High Rise

A man and his wife lived on the 25th floor of a high rise block. There were some peculiar circumstances about the way they used the lift.

The woman used it in the ordinary way, going up to and down from the 25th floor and when they were together the man did the same. When the man was by himself, however, he never went above the 15th floor by lift and always walked up the rest. He often went up all the way if there was anybody else in the lift but if he was alone he would never go above the 15th floor. There could be a thousand explanations for this but there is one simple, uncomplicated answer and that is what you are asked to annoy me by finding.

See Answer No. 63.

K.12 Double Fault?

The little boy was in trouble with his mother. "You've got your jersey on inside out *and* back to front, that's two things wrong in putting on one garment."

"That's not fair," said the father, "it's only one thing wrong."

The mother was certainly right, the jersey was back to front and it *was* inside out but the father was right also, this only involved one mistake. Can you explain this?

See Answer No. 67.

K.13 Two Right Handers

"Tommy," said the father, "I want you to help your Daddy. You'll need a pair of overalls and, it's a cold day, you'd better put on this pair of gloves."

"I can't wear these, Daddy."

"Why not?"

"They won't fit properly, they are both right-hand gloves, Daddy."

"Use your brains, you silly boy. Here let me fix it." The father took the gloves and in a second or two transformed them into a pair of handed gloves. How did the father convert the gloves from two right-handed gloves to a handed pair in a few seconds?

See Answer No. 71.

K.14   Brostles and Brongs

I have in my hand a brostle. It is my name for a solid object. You will find its name in the dictionary. A brostle has peculiar properties. Every brostle has 4 brongs on it. Brongs are also tangible, visible objects. I can take a sharp knife and cut off a brong from my brostle and hold the brostle in one hand and the brong in the other. I do not, however, reduce the number of brongs on the object. I actually increase it by two, making 6. Contradictorily and simultaneously, the brostle in my hand *has only 4 brongs on it*. How can this mystery be explained? What is a brostle? What is a brong?

See Answer No. 76.

K.15   The Hunter's Return

This is a really evil kickself problem. Obvious — when you know the answer — nasty, tricky and wicked. Definitely dirty pool.

The hunter starts from a certain point, marches exactly due south for one mile, turns and marches exactly east for one mile and then turns again and marches exactly north for one mile to arrive back at the spot he started from. Wait! I have no desire to know the colour of the bear he shoots at that point because there are no bears within five hundred miles. You see, I have kept back the nasty bit for the last. Before he started, there were another two hunters each standing at a point a mile away from the first one and not in the same place. And they all, together, march south, east and north, in exactly the same way that the first one did, and each of them arrives back at the point from which he started.

Your simple problem is to locate three points from which the three separated hunters started.

See Answer No. 83.

K.16   Why Do the Gods Hate Kansas?

"The Gods Hate Kansas" is the title of a science fiction story written by John Campbell. It results from a curious discovery concerning meteorites. At one time it was thought that all these Godly missiles were of iron but it gradually became clear that there were a few non-ferrous, stony, ones. As scientists searched more and more widely for evidence of this heavenly pelting they finally came to investigate the meteoric crop from the rich, flat farmlands of Kansas. And then it was that the heavenly discrimination and partiality became apparent. The Kansas share of iron meteorites per unit area was similar to that elsewhere but the Gods, it seems, take a special delight in pelting at the Unfortunate State with stony ones. In Kansas the stony missile fall, so to speak, per square kilometre is higher than anywhere else and about equal to that of iron ones. Isaac Asimov frankly admits that he was not smart enough to solve this problem at the time but later, he tells us, enlightenment came. That which puzzles the Great Brain, even for a time, is not to be sneered at as a problem.

The solver is invited to explain why the distribution of meteorites has this strange property. Iron meteorites are most common and distributed reasonably evenly, stony meteorites are much less common but in Kansas their frequency is about the same as that of iron ones. There is a simple kickself solution, what is the explanation?

See Answer No. 87.

Visualisation

The power of three-dimensional visualisation varies considerably between people. Some people of very high intelligence are not at all good at manipulating three-dimensional images in their mind. Here is a kickself problem which sounds deceptively simple but which, I desperately hope, will get you all confused.

K.17   Cubist? Diagonalist?

This is a test of your power for three-dimensional visualisation. You have to solve this without the aid of a drawing, if you are to get full marks.

Imagine a perfect cube. Imagine it to be made of Cheddar cheese. Now imagine a sharp knife. You are to bisect the cube by a single plane cut, whose central axis shall be the whole of one of the cube's long, three-dimensional diagonals.

A. The solver has to "evolve from his inner consciousness" without making a drawing the shape of the cut surface.

See Answer No. 95.

B. The solver must mentally count all the surfaces on the bisected cube and give the number.

See Answer No. 70.

Answering the
Unanswerable Question

All is riddle, and the key to a riddle is another riddle.

Emmerson, *Illusions*

The Unanswerable Quickly and Correctly Answered

Humility, I have always claimed, is nothing to be proud of. In the early part of my career I adopted a self-effacing posture and gave the practice of normal and proper humility a really thorough trial. It was difficult to suppress my underlying self-confidence, but I succeeded. The universal response to my humility was complete apathy. The general view then seemed to be that it was fully justified. So I gave it up, showed some tentative signs of self-confidence and risked a few timid toots on my own trumpet. People, I found, take you at your own valuation. Since then I have never looked back. Expecting and getting a few rebuffs I gradually climbed to my present heights of presumptuous over-confidence and I am satisfied with the results.

I am a bit like the man who was observed going along the street saying to every pretty woman he passed, "Will you sleep with me, darling?" He was collecting a lot of indignant stares and even an occasional face-slapping. I asked him if this was his usual habit, he said, "Yes."

"You must get a lot of rebuffs," I said.

"Yes, but I get a lot of the other too."

And all this building up to my firm declaration that though I cannot be sure I have the right answer to *answerable* questions, I give here the answer to several that have been held to be unanswerable for a long time.

First we must ask what we *mean* by answering questions?

It is an error to think that the answering of *any* question is a yes or no affair. When you get right down to it, there is no answer to any question which is unquestionably satisfactory. For a numerical question we might always ask for a few more decimal points or a slightly better definition. Our answers are always "good enough for our purpose". For a numerical question, we ought always to be able to give an answer which sets high and low limits to the estimate. I remember being much impressed when my friend Professor John Good, in one mathematical discussion, said "So the answer is around 3½ million multiplied by or divided by a thousand." An answer of even this imprecision can sometimes be better than nothing.

There are, of course, those who will argue that to questions in logic there are unequivocal answers but I believe that even these can be questioned. Firstly, logic is made manifest in words and symbols and these acquire their meaning because of a consensus, not a unanimity.

Every logical concept is, at least to a limited degree, a "fuzzy set" in this sense, if no other, and to that extent is attended by some uncertainty, that is, it is not beyond doubt.

Once we admit that all answers have, whether it is explicitly stated or not, limits of certainty, we may see that within sufficiently broad limits, so-called unanswerable questions can be answered. Also, it follows that within sufficiently narrow limits *no* question is answerable. We need to know the limits before we can decide upon the answerability.

Now therefore I give the bolder among my readers the opportunity to join me upon this summit of presumptious arrogance by answering (quickly and correctly if you please) the following UQs (unanswerable questions).

UQ.1 Don't Ask

Two Jews meet again after many years.

"So long you don't see me, you don't ask me how I am?"

"So, all right, how are you?"

"Don't ask me!"

The Japanese have a set reply to unanswerable questions which freely translated means "Unask".

This is to say that this cop-out is *not* available to the reader and a prompt answer to these unanswerable questions *is* required. So here is the first U.Q.

Can unanswerable questions be answered?

See Answer No. 5.

UQ.2 Irresistible, Immovable

An indignant buyer returned to the horse dealer.

"I want my money back, that horse you sold me is stone blind."

"What makes you think that?"

"He keeps walking into walls."

"He ain't blind, he just don't give a damn."

Here the wall was a relatively "immovable object", and this brings us to the supposedly unanswerable question, "What happens when an irresistible force meets an immovable object?"

I insist that there is an answer which is sensible in terms of the question. Think! What happens?

See Answer No. 11.

UQ.3 Chicken/Egg Priority

A vast crowd assembled to see the skyscraper climber do his stuff. The respectful crowd parted to let him through. His pack on his back, he confidently took his first step on a crevice on the face of the twenty-storey building. The crowd was tense and silent as he climbed but, as he carefully considered each grip, he noticed a strange note in the noise from the crowd. Could it be tittering? Yes, they were laughing. Clinging precariously he glanced down and noticed that he was being followed by a drunk. He climbed on, ignored by the crowd, who laughed, cheered or shouted in alarm according to their nature at the antics of the drunken man. Miraculously, he reached the top soon after the official climber. The latter thought that now it was his turn, for the pack on his back was a parachute. He stepped to the brink, smiled, spread his arms with a dramatic gesture, leaped off, pulled the cord, and was soon sailing towards the earth with arms folded and a smile of triumph on his face.

Half-way down the drunk hurtled passed him. As he did so he shouted "Chicken". Fortunately the story stops at that point, the point at which it brings me tortuously, to the next puzzle, that of the chicken and the egg.

I have never been able to understand why this is given as an example of an unanswerable question. The answer ought to be absolutely obvious to any thinking person, so I pose it again. Think about it. Which came first, the chicken or the egg?

See Answer No. 18.

UQ.4   The Length of that Stupid Piece of Blasted String

Do you like string? During the war I used to mix with a young crowd in a South London pub and to confuse newcomers to the group it was our practice earnestly to ask this question. I would take some young girl who had been introduced to the group, take her aside, sit down, look earnestly into her eyes and ask, "Do you like string?" A somewhat confused reply would be followed by an enthusiastic diatribe from me in which gradually the other afficionados would join.

"I hate the brown, rough string." "So do I but I love that thin, hard, white string, don't you?" "I'm absolutely mad about tangled string, especially tangled *grey* string," and so it continued. "I love coarse string." "I just can't live without dirty string" and so it would go on, the "in-group" crudely demonstrating its interiority, so to speak. After a time, which varies with intelligence, the tyro sees that the others are stringing him along, joins the game and becomes a string-buff.

Which brings us to the supposedly unanswerable question "How long is a piece of string?" The reader is brusquely ordered to answer this question.

See Answer No. 24.

UQ.5 When "Above Average" is the Norm!

I had a visit from a journalist who seemed to want to make the most of Mensa. He started to talk about the Geniuses Club. I pointed out that Mensa membership was open to anyone who was in the top 2% of the population for measured intelligence and that there were about a million people in England who could qualify. I was very sensitive of the great virtues of the British people but I was doubtful that we could claim a million geniuses.

"Ah! Mr. Serebriakoff", he said, "but surely it's very well known that the vast majority of people are far below average intelligence?"

"Well — half of them are below average," I conceded.

But — almost every man and woman has a supply of a certain material thing. Very few people have less than the average number of these objects and the vast majority have more than the average number. How can this be? What are the things concerned?

See Answer No. 31.

UQ.6 The Most Difficult Question in the World

An Irishman in Limerick asked the Kerry man to help him check that the trafficator was working on his motorcar.

"Just stand behind the car and tell me if it is working," said the motorist.

"Sure and I will."

"I am putting the right trafficator on now. Is it working?"

"It's working — it ain't — it's working — it ain't . . ."

This was not a difficult question. But *this* is impossibly difficult. A man went into a bar and because he had no money, said to the barman, "If I answer the most difficult question in the world, will you give me a double whiskey?" The barman was intrigued. A local worthy was appointed as judge and the thirsty pauper continued, "The most difficult question in the world is: What is the most difficult question in the world," and the answer is "The question; what is the most difficult question in the world?" So I have answered the most difficult question in the world. Gimme me drink!

Question: Had he won his drink?

See Answer No. 37.

UQ.7 Give the Difference Between Two Unknowns (and quick about it)

As a general rule I am fairly tolerant but there are people that I find unpleasant and questions that I find unreasonable. There was, for instance, the crowd of commuters who travelled in the same railway carriage and one of them, as nasty a piece of work as you will find, used to amuse his fellow travellers by tricks and jokes of various kinds. One day he intrigued everyone by passing round a small piece of putty-like substance and asking people if they could guess what the material was. The travellers took it in turns, fingered it, prodded it and rolled it. Some had no idea and others made a guess. "A new plastic." "Some sort of putty." "Stale toothpaste." "Plasticine." "It's just a piece of dough." After much puzzling, they finally gave up. "Well, what is it?"

"I've no idea."

"Well, where did you get it?"

"I found it up my nose."

An unreasonable and unpleasant question, and a very dirty trick.

This next question is not quite so unpleasant and insanitary but it is equally unreasonable and unfair.

We have all seen thousands of different tables of numbers, tables that have been concocted for various purposes. On almost all these tables you will obviously find a definite relationship between the terms but among this great family of tables there is one whose very existence one might be tempted to question. Those acquainted with the mysterious world of statistics, the science of uncertainty, the art by which we try to measure how little we know, will have become innured to the idea of a Table of Random Numbers. Serious adults, trained professional people, sit calmly down to fill page after page with an utterly unrelated series of random digits. We might define a table of random numbers as a series of digits between 0 and 9 which is not a series, in that it is such that no sub-set of the numbers will give the slightest clue as to what the next number will be.

Mathematicians tell us that there are things that you can do with such a table which you cannot do with any other kind of table and I mean to put their nonsensical statement to the test. This is my wicked question. You are not allowed to refer to a table of random numbers, you have to work entirely by guesswork. Without having the faintest idea what the numbers are, my peremptory demand is that you take a very large set of these random digits, thousands of them. Compare each digit with its neighbour, observe the difference, then answer the following two questions:

Question A: What is the average difference between two random digits?

See Answer No. 43.

Question B: (And it is up to you to decide if this is a different question), deduct each digit from its right-hand neighbour, what is the average difference?

See Answer No. 48.

UQ.8   Pseudo Non-Randomness

The idea of randomness gives much trouble to logicians, mathematicians and philosophers. No one seems to be able to define what randomness is and all attempts to construct a logical theory of randomness by one learned gent are gleefully picked apart by all the other learned gents. One particularly annoying learned gent pointed out that any of the incommensurables like π or $\sqrt{2}$ can only be set down as an infinite series of decimal digits. You can take whole slices from this series at random, and there is no way to tell that they are not random although in fact there is a logical relationship running through the lot. These are called pseudo random numbers. I want to ask readers to think about pseudo *non*-random numbers. I give a modest example below:

Consider this series   789789789789789789

Now this question is downright evil, the set of random digits *might* contain this as an element. Calculate the probability that this is part of a random series?

See Answer No. 54.

UQ.9   The Odds? Evens!

The odds that you can guess the answer to this are *evens* because there are only two answers. But you have to do more than get it right, you have to show that your answer is not a guess. We live in a society that is riven, we are told, by class divisions. I am about to aggravate this divisive by creating yet another. I divide all people into that honoured elite who shook hands an even number of times last year and that deprived underprivileged class who shook hands an odd number of times last year. I ask you to forget the undeserving elite and to concentrate on the latter unhappy group.

My question is: the number of these unfortunates, the odd handshakers; is that number an odd number or an even number? and, much more important, how do you know?

See Answer No. 59.

Conceptual Conflict in Multi-Dimensional Space

The intellectual is *engagé,* committee, enlisted. What everyone else is unwilling to admit, namely that ideas and abstractions are of signal importance, he imperatively feels.

Richard Hofstadter
Anti-Intellectualism in American Life (1963)

We, the literate, tend to reduce all problems to a two-dimensional form if we can. This is only partly because some of us are not too good at three-dimensional thinking. (The descendants of tree leapers with stereoscopic vision, we ought to be very good at 3D conceptualisation.) The problem is the way we are educated. We have found so much of our enlightenment and education on the flat surfaces of books and papers: screens and blackboards, that we try, just from habit, to translate all problems into 2D terms.

But many problems are only made more difficult by this translation, by trying to think with a dimension missing.

Mercilessly exploiting this weakness I now intend to provoke you into a struggle with some multi-dimensional puzzles and games. First I shall lift you into the third dimension. Then to ensure myself against the possible humiliation of your surmounting this I shall go on to propose games in four and even *five* dimensions. You read on at your own risk!

Three-Dimensional Noughts and Crosses

The Great Brains who encounter and combat the Great Difficulties of this Nasty Tricky Book will no doubt look upon the normal two-dimensional game Noughts and Crosses as an amusement for Densans.

Three-dimensional Noughts and Crosses can be played on computers and on plastic structures. What I present here is a way of playing the 3D game on 2D paper. Much more difficult!

I have opened up the 27 cell cube the game is played on and three cubes are shown which can be photocopied. That done you can drive your best friend down to humiliating defeats on this wickedly complex game.

The rules have to be modified to reduce the advantage of the first player — they are simple — the game is not. Watch the scoring — it is easy to miss lines.

One drawing shows an example of possibles lines, "down", "across" and "through". It also shows diagonals, short and long.

The other drawing shows the completion, unlikely, of a "plane" giving 8 lines.

I was going to tell you the number of "lines" altogether but that would be helpful so instead I pose that as a puzzle.
Question: How many "lines", of three adjoining cells, face to face, edge to edge, or corner to corner, in a straight line are there in a three-dimensional Noughts and Crosses Cube?

See Answer No. 100.

Now to the game.

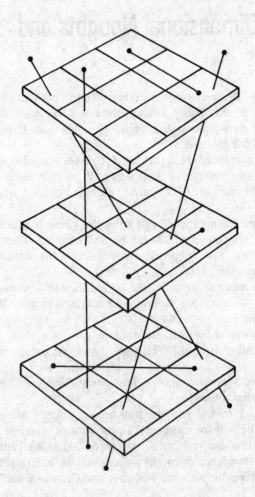

Lines

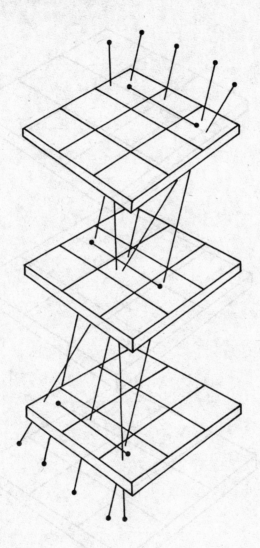

A Plane (8 lines)

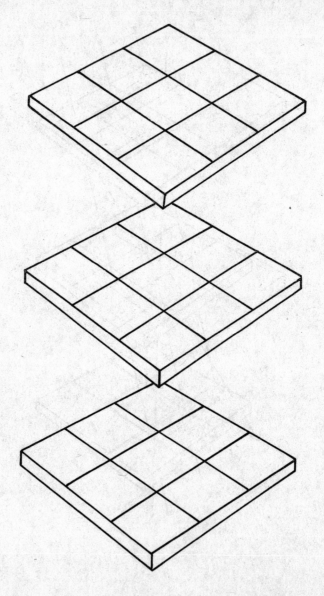

Some blanks to copy

NOUGHTS AND CROSSES

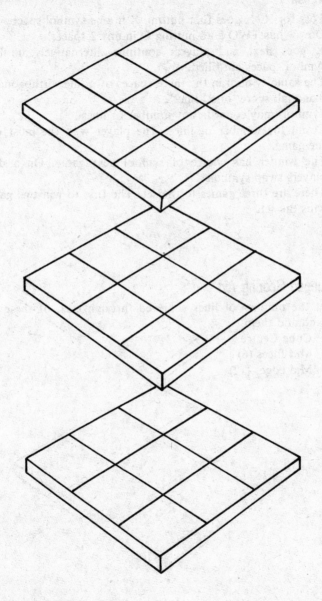

to play the game

The Rules

1. Toss for X, X goes first putting X in one symbol space.
2. O now has TWO goes putting O in any 2 spaces.
3. X goes next and players continue alternatively until all symbol spaces are filled.
4. The same symbol in the three spaces of a line, orthogonal or diagonal, scores one "line".
5. Symbols may count in any number of lines.
6. Count the number of lines. The player with the most wins the game.
7. The winner has choice of symbol next game. On a draw players swap symbols.
8. There are three games to the set. The first to win two games wins the set.

Begrudged Scoring Aid

Count the number of lines achieved through each of these key cells and add them.

       Cube Centre
       Mid faces (6)
       Mid edges (12)

Multi-Dimensional Oxo

This is the crowning horror of the book. This wicked world, as I said, has only a meagre three-orthogonal dimension. We are conditioned to thinking and planning in these three. As a refinement of your self-torture I am now proposing to tempt you to play, with some unfortunate companion, Noughts and Crosses in the unfamiliar world of four dimensions.

Let me start with a skippable diversion.

The Three Partial Anglophones

An Anglophone is speaking to three who were sadly only partial Anglophones and therefore the rightful target and butt of all Anglophones.

Anglophone (in perfect English spoken in a well-modulated voice and an upper-middle-class accent): Have you any children?

First Partial Anglophone: No. I am sorry of it, but misfortunately my wife is impregnable.

Second Partial Anglophone: Please to excuse it, the unexcellent English at my friend. He is meaning the women from him is unbearable.

Third Partial Anglophone (laughing): Is funny the mistakes on my two friends. Is meaning my friend his lady is inconceivable.

With that I invite you to enter a world which like the Third Partial Anglophone's wife, is inconceivable or at any rate Only Partially Conceivable.

We Enter the World of the Only Partially Conceivable

So far, my vexed and tortured readers have had to struggle with problems related only to the three-dimensional world of their experience. The answers to the questions have been difficult but at least they have been conceivable.

But the human mind is an instrument that can reach beyond the limits of its experience. It has created mental worlds, and explored their shape, form and dimensions.

We live in a world of three dimensions, each at right angles to the others. Einstein and others have seen time as being a fourth dimension at right angles to all the other three.

Irrational numbers and other concepts which conflict with experience and the unlimited extension of dimensions seem to be more than helpful, they seem to be necessary to the elucidation of many practical problems.

Mathematicians have explored multi-dimensional worlds and one of the mysteries of the universe is the fact that sometimes these thought patterns, these adventures into worlds beyond our experience, yield results which turn out to have predictive value in the real world around us.

So your first problem is one which will lead the way into the unexperienced but partially conceivable world of many dimensions.

Mental Breakout from Three Dimensions

I puzzled for a long time about this problem, the answer at each stage seemed to be clear but I found it very difficult to get a logical scheme from which it could be predicted. When eventually I was told the simple Kickself answer, my ankles were black and blue for weeks after it. Such a kicking!

I was sitting at breakfast with my friend, Clive Sinclair, and I began to tell him about the problem. "I've no idea" he said and went on eating his breakfast.

But something had clicked somewhere in the ramifications of that considerable brain. He disappeared and returned with a book which he threw on the breakfast table and said, "Page 153, I think."

On page 153 was the infuriatingly simple answer which I failed to find and which I gleefully invite you to look for.

Walking along this track will lead us into n-dimensional space by easy stages — I am getting soft.

How Many Bounds?

How many b-dimensional bounds (vertices, edges, faces) are there in a d-dimensional cube?

Reluctantly, I will give you a little help along the way.

We are looking at boundaries. In a zero-dimensional figure, a point, there is one bound only, one vertex, one could say. Pull the point apart to make a one-dimensional figure, a line, and it must have two bounds, its ends. It has two one-dimensional boundaries and one line or a two-dimensional boundary.

Now take the line, in your imagination, and pull it sideways so that you have a square. You now have doubled the number of vertices or zero-dimensional bounds, you have 4, and you also have 4 one-dimensional bounds, edges. And you have 1 two-dimensional bound, a plane.

Now, you have to climb off the paper!

Your simple task is to take the plane that you have made and lift it off the paper, mentally, at the same time as leaving it behind, let it undergo a mitosis to make a cube. Lifting it off the paper, its four corners will trace four edges, two-dimensional bounds, and with the 4 you started with and the 4 you finish with, you will have 12 edges, two-dimensional bounds. You have duplicated the one-dimensional bounds, the vertices, so you will have 8 of those. And you will have 6 faces, two-dimensional bounds, where you had one before. Your 4 edges will have traced a new face each and the starting and finishing positions will be two more.

I hope you don't get the idea. Now you have to proceed on your own. Tease your three-dimensional cube out into a fourth dimension, at right angles to the other three; never mind the obvious laws of Euclidean geometry. Remembering that we had a new kind of boundary each time we proceed to the next step, we shall expect there to be one hypercube, a certain number of boundary cubes, planes, edges, and vertices.

Oxo One

So how many are there of each of these boundary features?

See Answer No. 6.

Oxo Two

More important, what is the simple underlying rule which enables us to say the number of one, two, three, four, five, six, seven, eight-dimensional boundaries for $1, 2, 3, 4, 5, 6, 7, 8$-dimensional hypercubes, hyper-hypercubes, and hyper-hyper-hypercubes?

The answer is infuriatingly simple — Once you know it!

See Answer No. 12.

So! On to the Horrors of Hyper-Dimensional Oxo

In some versions of multi-dimensional Noughts and Crosses the usual three cells have been increased to four cells but I retain the three cells but set the player to fill in planes, not lines, to find lines would be too easy — and too much advantage to the first player.

How do we do it?

To represent the fourth dimension graphically, I show two opened-up noughts and crosses cubes on either side of one similar to what you have already seen in the last puzzle. When we made the three-dimensional noughts and crosses, we did it by putting a layer of nine cells above and below the nine cells of the normal two-dimensional game.

We now have to represent a situation in which we place two cubes on either side of this central cube but do so in such a way that each cell in each of the outside cubes is in face to face contact with its counterpart in the central cube. One could get a line through the three centre cubes, for instance, or the three top far left-corner cubes, for instance.

One can draw a diagonal from the near left bottom-corner of the left cube through the centre of the centre cube to the far top right-corner of the right-hand cube.

But in this game we are not seeking to complete lines but planes.

The Rules

Here are the rules for hypercube noughts and crosses.
1. Toss for "X", X goes first, putting his "X" in any one cell.
2. The second player has choice of whether game is for one, three or five planes (for advanced players) and he now has two turns (to compensate for the big advantage of the first turn).
3. After that the players continue alternately in the usual way until one player has completed one plane.
4. The players continue until one gets the target number of planes, that player wins.
5. A plane is scored when any array of nine cells is filled with the same symbol. An array must be of 9 face neighbours, 9 edge neighbours or 9 vertex neighbours in one plane, which may be in *any* pair of the four dimensions.
6. Cells may form part of plurality of planes.
7. If the target is not achieved the game is a draw and the players swap symbols. A player that reaches the target number of planes wins and has the choice of symbols for the next game.

But before you start off, here is another problem:

Oxo Three Hypercube Planes

How many different planes are there in a hypercube?

See Answer No. 29.

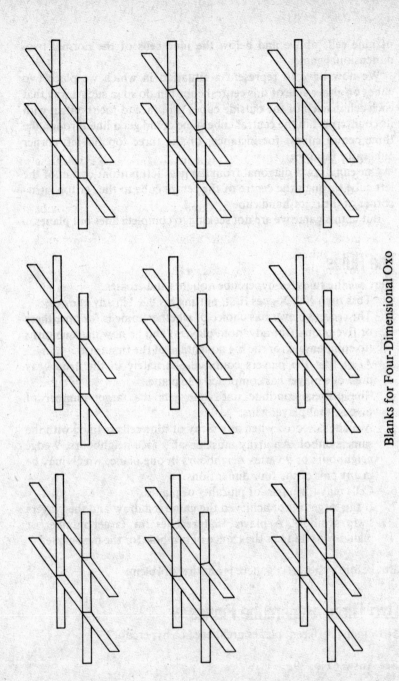

Blanks for Four-Dimensional Oxo

Five-Dimensional Noughts and Crosses

If you attempt to play this, you must be a genius or mad or both. Taking the charitable assumption that you are a genius, I shall abandon any attempt to help your imagination by representing in three dimensions and simply lay out the problem in two.

In the diagram, the central section B, is a simplified representation of the lay-out of three cubes to make a hypercube as in four-dimensional noughts and crosses.

You have to imagine that the groups of nine cells are stacked above each other.

Following the same principle as we did to get from three to four dimensions, we have simply duplicated that and drawn on either side at A and C a further hypercube to make up a five-dimensional hyper-hypercube. The game is played like four-dimensional noughts and crosses but if you want to face a real challenge, you can try to complete a three-dimensional cube instead of a number of planes. Or you can play for the first plane or for the first two or three or five planes. There are ten hypercubes and forty cubes in this hyper-hypercube so, carefully selecting your opponents, with artfulness, skill, brains and patience you should, to my fury and annoyance, succeed in licking the pants off someone at hyperspace noughts and crosses. Go ahead, bad luck!

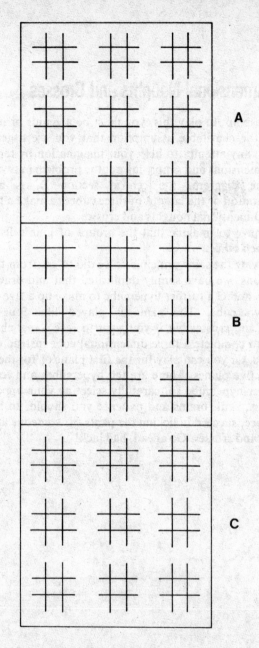

Blanks for Five-Dimensional Oxo

The Answers
(if you need them)

Each question has an answer number, different from the question number so as to reduce the risk of advertent or inadvertent peeking.

The answer number is mixed up relative to the question order so look at the answer number and ignore the question number.

Answer No. 1

T.21 Turning the Golden Cone

Answer: 84.4%. Everything depends on the point where he parts off the point of the cone. A well-established mathematical rule tells us that he has to part off at a third of the height of the cone and at this point when he turns it off, he will get the maximum volume. (Those like me who did not know the rule can proceed by trial and error with a calculator or use calculus.)

We do not need to know the base or height of the cone as they cancel out as follows:

Let H be height of cone, R be radius of the base of cone. At the half-point cut the radius of the cylinder is halved at the ⅓ cut point it will be ⅔. The ratio between the volume of the "ingot" and the optimum volume obtainable is:

the ratio $\quad \dfrac{\pi \left(\frac{R}{2}\right)^2 \frac{H}{2}}{\pi \left(\frac{2R}{3}\right)^2 \frac{H}{3}} = \dfrac{(\frac{1}{2})^3}{\frac{1}{3}(\frac{2}{3})^2} = 0.84375$

after cancelling out.

Answer No. 2

S.1 Answer: 24. These are the prime numbers (those which are not divisible by any other integer except 1) with 1 added in each case.

Answer No. 3

F.1 The Professor's Table-Cloth
Too many books spoil the cloth.

Answer No. 4

K.1 Time to Strike
4 seconds — the time between the clapper striking the bell for the first peal and the second one is 2 seconds, 2 seconds later it strikes for the third peal. Do not be confused by the lingering sound — I said strike!

114

Answer No. 5

UQ.1 Don't Ask

Yes and No. No, because if they are answered they are not unanswerable and Yes, because you can answer any question if you do not care whether the answer is correct or even relevant, or again No because . . . etc.

Answer No. 6

Oxo One   How Many Bounds?

16 vertices, 32 edges, 24 faces, 8 boundary cubes and 1 hypercube.

Answer No. 7

T.23   The Square on the Diagonal

Answer: 31.25mm

The simple rule is that for each two steps of the series the side of the square is halved so that the 11th step is 1/32nd of the original square.

Answer No. 8

S.2   Answer: 73.

The rule is multiply by 2 and add 7 alternately.

Answer No. 9

F.2   Muddled Hearses

A hearse of another killer.

Answer No. 10

K.2   The Jilted Witch

She had jammed the clapper with packed snow which melted during the ceremony. No one noticed the damp patch below the bell.

Answer No. 11

UQ.2   Irresistible, Immovable

My friend, Isaac Asimov, says that any universe which contains an immovable object cannot also contain an irresistible force and vice versa. But as Isaac has not examined this universe in real detail, let alone all possible universes, we could put this another way and say that he cannot conceive of a universe which contains both. So, in the same kind of terms as the question is posed, we can answer the question very simply. What happens when an irresistible force meets an immovable object is an *inconceivable event*.

Answer No. 12

Oxo Two   So What is the Rule?

The Answer can be obtained from the simple polynomial $(2x + 1)^n$

Let me show this for the first few stages:

$$2x + 1 \quad \text{2 ends 1 line in a line}$$

multiply

$$2x + 1$$

$$\underline{2x + 1}$$

$$\underline{4x^2 + 2x \quad\quad}$$

$$4x^2 + 4x + 1 \quad \text{4 corners 4 edges 1 face in a square}$$

multiply again

$$\underline{2x + 1}$$

$$4x^2 + 4x + 1$$

$$\underline{8x^3 + 8x^2 + 2x \quad\quad}$$

$$8x^3 + 12x^2 + 6x + 1 \quad \text{8 vertices 12 edges 6 faces one cube in a cube}$$

A Norwegian Mensa friend, Cecilia Irgens, put this on to her computer and found that, for instance, for 10 dimensions there is one hyper-hyper. . .hyper-cube. 20, 9-dimensional bounds, 180, 8-dimensional bounds, 960, 7-dimensional bounds, 3,360, 6-dimensional bounds, 8,064, 5-dimensional bounds, 13,440, 4-dimensional bounds, 15,360, 3-dimensional bounds, 11,520, 2-dimensional bounds, 5,120, 1-dimensional bounds or edges and 1,024 vertices. Imagine that!

Answer No. 13

T.16   Pouring Puttonos

Question A: Oh, very simple but very foolish. Fill dent, freeze in refrigerator, fill hat and nip next door a bit fastish.

Answer No. 14

S.3   Answer: 30.

This series is the set of non-primes starting from 9. (Prime numbers are those which are not divisible by any other integer except 1.)

Answer No. 15

T.26   Escherism

The error will be seen at the co-ordinate 4D.

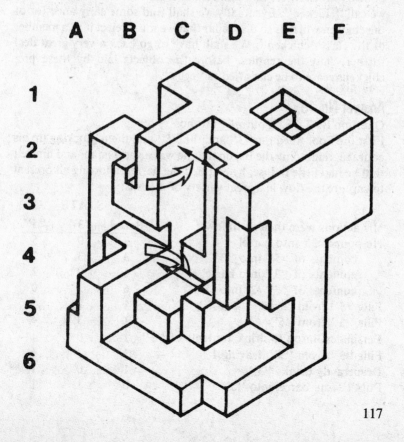

Answer No. 16

F.3 The Running Dogs
Many hounds make light work.

Answer No. 17

K.3 Hurried Barbers
30 minutes. One does one haircut and three shaves and the other does two haircuts.

Answer No. 18

UQ.3 Chicken/Egg Priority
There is absolutely no doubt that the egg came first. Let us go back through time, passing a succession of eggs and chickens on our way. Unless we reject the theory of evolution, we shall be looking at birds which differ more and more from that class of bird which we call "chicken". Eventually we shall find some early ancestor of the chicken which is so dissimilar that we must reject it as a member of the class "chicken". We shall have to go back a very great deal further, past the reptiles, before the objects laid by these pre-chickens cease to be classified as "eggs".

Answer No. 19

Question B: T.16 Pouring Puttonos
First the Fool filled the "3" and the "5" and then, plucking up his courage, reminding the Baron that he was a sportsman, and himself that he had little to lose, he emptied the barrel, allowing all present to capture the flow in a great variety of utensils.

	STATE		
His actions were then as follows:	Barrel	"3"	"5"
He pours "3" into barrel	3	0	5
contents of "5" into "3"	3	3	2
contents of "3" into barrel	6	0	2
contents of "5" (2) into "3"	6	2	0
Fills "5" from barrel	1	2	5
Fills "3" from "5"	1	3	4
Persuades Baron to drink contents of "3"	1	0	4
Fills "3" from "5" leaving 1	1	3	1
Desperately drinks "3"	1	0	1
Puts 1 from barrel into "3"	0	1	1

118

which was what the Baron and everybody else who was still awake had asked to be done — though none remembered it.

Answer No. 20

S.4   Answer: 1.
Rule — starting with 22, we alternately subtract 2 and divide by 2.

Answer No. 21

T.25   Slow Burn or Shooting
His reply was: "I shall die for days over the small fire." The dictator called in his wise men to solve the dilemma and several died over the small fire. It did not help them finding the answer. Time passed and the dictator turned to other problems and thus the liar remained unpunished.

Answer No. 22

F.4   Cattle Call
Pat calling the cattle bloke.

Answer No. 23

K.4   Blind Man's Socks
A: 36. With 35 he could have 17 red, 17 blue and only 1 green.

Answer No. 24

UQ.4   The Length of that Stupid Piece of Blasted String
The sensible answer to this question is to try to define the limits. If we want our answer to be safe against contradiction, we must set the lower limit, fairly low, nothing much shorter than, say, a centimetre, is likely to be classified as a piece of string. It might be a piece of fibre or something but not a piece of string in normal parlance.

So what is the upper limit? This must obviously be dictated by the practicalities of string manufacture and by the convenience of handling. Without making an investigation at a string factory, we can guess that it is unlikely that such a factory would install cranes above 1 ton capacity and since the string must be made on to some reel or spool, it is unlikely that a single piece would be much over a tonne. Working out the limits between string and thread, we can equally guess that no one would classify a material as string at a diameter below 1.5mm and fine string is likely to be dense or it will fall apart so we can guess that a density of .7 as being the worst case. Calculating all this out we come to an answer. Not a very precise one but one which is a good deal more precise than many answers which are confidently advanced in astronomy and physics.

The length of a piece of string is:

$$5822195 \pm 5822194.99 \text{ metres}$$

At 0.7kg/litre estimate of volume $\ngtr$ $\dfrac{1000\text{kg}}{0.7\text{kg/litre}}$

1429 litres or approx 1.429m^3

$\therefore$ maximum length $\ngtr$ $\dfrac{\text{Volume}}{\text{area}} = \dfrac{1.429\text{m}^3}{\pi\,(0.625\text{mm})^2} =$

So the string is $\ngtr$ than 11644.39km $\nless$ 1cm which can be expressed as above.

Answer No. 25
T.4   Message from an Incommunicado
There was one other thing that must have gone in and out of the cell which was not mentioned in the explanation. Air. This small cell must have had a ventilation system and the prisoner's problem was how was he to impress some kind of message onto the emitted air?

He hit upon the idea of regulating his exercise. The room being small, he could, by taking violent exercise in periodic bouts, raise the carbon dioxide content of the air which must have been emitted at some point.

His accomplice, knowing the intelligence of the prisoner, located the point where the stale air was emitted from the ventilation system and found, by good luck, that it very sensibly included a meter which monitored carbon dioxide content. By watching the variations of this meter reading over some time he soon detected that the pattern of exercise bouts, long and short, constituted a version of the morse code, so information was passed on to the Unfriendly Power in this gymnastic code.

Answer No. 26

S.5   Answer: 131,072.
The start is 4, and the transform rule is, moving right, we take half the square. (We multiply the number by itself and divide by two.)

Answer No. 27

F.5   Sawing Trays
Can't saw the wood for the trays.

Answer No. 28

T.24   The Golden Ball and the Oxford Professors
Answer: The second professor was not wise. The proportion of swarf to paperweight varies with the height of the cylinder (obviously). The bulkiest cylinder is to be obtained when the ratio, radius of cylinder to radius of sphere is $\sqrt{\frac{2}{3}} = 0.816495$. This gives the ratio of volumes, cylinder to sphere as 57.73502% which means the second professor has to be content with only 422.65 grammes of golden swarf out of the kilogramme ball.

The detailed working follows:

$$\frac{\text{volume of cylinder}}{\text{volume of sphere}} \quad \frac{c}{s} = \frac{\pi r^2 2h}{\frac{4}{3}\pi R^3}$$

If we let R = 1 then $\dfrac{c}{s} = \dfrac{3r^2 2h}{4} = 1.5r^2h$

From Pythagorus $h^2 = R^2 - r^2$

$\therefore h = \sqrt{1-r^2}$ $\therefore \dfrac{c}{s} = 1.5r^2\sqrt{1-r^2}$

Calculus or some experiment on a pocket calculator establishes that the optimum ratio $\frac{r}{R} = \sqrt{\frac{2}{3}} = 0.8164965$.

This gives, by substitution, the ratio $\frac{c}{s}$ as 0.5773502 so the cylinder weighs 577.35 grammes which gives 422.65 grammes of swarf for the unwise second professor.

The ratio $\frac{c}{s}$ is also the ratio $\frac{h}{R}$ or $\sqrt{\frac{1}{3}}$.

Answer No. 29

Oxo Three Hypercube Planes
Answer: 123. The answer is best approached by looking at all the cells that can be the middle of a plane and counting for each of them the number of planes of which they can be the middle.

Answer No. 30

K.4 Blind Man's Socks
B: 4. With 3 he could have one of each colour.

Answer No. 31

UQ.5 When "Above Average" is the Norm!
Fingers, toes, arms, legs, ears — they all come within this category. Amputees and those born short of these extremities are in a small minority and a congenital excess is very rare indeed. So if we divide the total number of fingers, for instance, in the world by the total number of people, we should get an answer less than ten (9.99 something). So nearly everybody must have above that average number of fingers.

Answer No. 32

T.5   The Evil Ways of Augustus Henry Simpkins

Simpkins had bought identical tins of peaches and tomatoes in a different shop. Chuckling fiendishly to himself, he had carefully steamed off and switched the labels. When he was handed a tin of properly labelled tomatoes he called them peaches until, during the subsequent discussions with the assistant and the manager, he found an opportunity to switch the tin for the wrongly labelled one he was carrying.

Now that you know that, you may refer to puzzle No. T.27 "Simpkin's Come-Uppance". There you will learn how this dreadful business was resolved, justice done and brilliant intelligence displayed by the forces of Law and Order.

Answer No. 33

S.6   Answer: 1.
The rule is alternately deduct three and take the square root.

Answer No. 34

T.2   Motor Boat
2⅔ minutes (2 minutes 40 seconds)
Speed downstream 1 km per minute.
Speed back ½ km per minute, therefore the current makes a quarter of a km per minute difference, so his boat speed is three-quarters of a km per minute. 2 km divided by three-quarters of a km per minute equals two and two-thirds minutes.

Answer No. 35

F.6   Red Mouth
Bott culling the betel plaque.

Answer No. 36

K.5   Cuts and Ends
The simplest answer is an elastic band or continuous V-belt, but it could be any torus.

Answer No. 37

UQ.6   The Most Difficult Question in the World
He got the drink for his sheer cheek but it did him no good.
Questions like, "What is the most difficult question in the world?"
are not very sensible questions and we must expect that the first law
of computers to apply, "Garbage in, garbage out".

Answer No. 38

T.27   Simpkin's Come-Uppance
There is no need to open the tin of peanuts which will be much
lighter than the others. This will eliminate one label too. By
opening any of the other tins, another label and another type of
contents will be eliminated so the labelling of the other two will be
obvious since there are only two labels left and two contents left
and we know that both tins are falsely labelled.

Answer No. 39

S.7   Answer: 2.
The integers in descending order are added each to its reciprocal,
the reciprocal of 1 is 1, so $1 + 1 = 2$.

Answer No. 40

F.7   Darwin's Gin
The hurried gin of the speeches.

Answer No. 41

T.22   Are Squearths *Really* All Nuphs?
1. It can, alas! it can.
2. No. If they are not nuphs there is no way they can be glops.
3. Yes, it must be a glop and it may be a gdynx.
The classification problem is best understood from the Venn
diagram opposite.

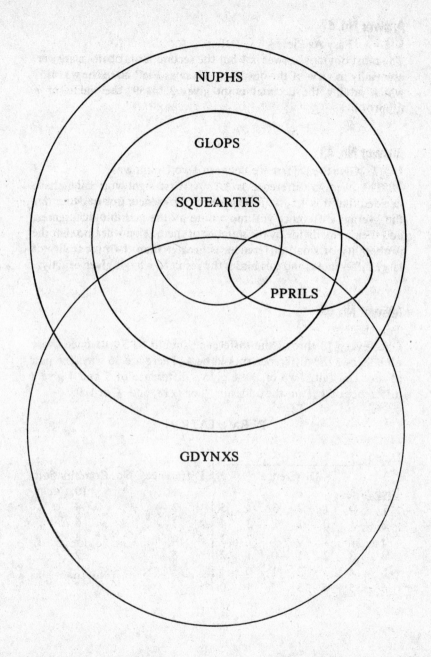

NUPHS

GLOPS

SQUEARTHS

PPRILS

GDYNXS

Answer No. 42

K.6   As Easy As Pie

The most obvious answer is 1 but the second most obvious answer, especially in view of the heading, "Easy as Pie" is 9 giving 314159 which adding the decimal point gives 3.14159, the value of π (approx).

Answer No. 43

UQ.7   Give the Difference Between Two Unknowns

A. The average difference is 3.3. At first sight you might have decided that it is 4.5, half the greatest difference. But to determine the average difference you must note all the possible differences, add them, and divide by the number of them. You will find that the probability of small differences is greater than the probability of large differences, and this biases the result to what is given exactly.

Answer No. 44

T.6   Dicing

Once every 18 throws the difference should be 5 and once every nine throws the difference should be 4. There are 36 ways the pair of dice can fall. Two of these give a difference of 5 and 4 give a difference of 4. Thus the odds are $\frac{2}{36}$ or 1/18; and $\frac{4}{36}$ or 1/9.

PERMUTATION

Dice 1	1	2	3	4	5	6		Difference	No. Combinations
			Difference					1	10
Dice 2								2	8
1	0	1	2	3	4	5		3	6
2	1	0	1	2	3	4		4	4
3	2	1	0	1	2	3		5	2
4	3	2	1	0	1	2			
5	4	3	2	1	0	1			
6	5	4	3	2	1	0			

Answer No. 45

S.8

The next three terms are 6, 2, 6.

The intervals of the prime numbers.

This series is the result of deducting each of the prime numbers from the next prime number above it in magnitude.

Answer No. 46

T.1   Sorting Scribbles

From the higgledy-piggledy arrangement you should have deduced that orientation does not matter. These are the classes, seven of them:

1	A, D, Q
2	B, N, R
3	C, M, O
4	F, H, T
5	I, L, S
6	J, K, U
7	G, P, E

Answer No. 47

K.7   "Head South Pardner"

5 miles. You must find the place on earth where the distance is maximum. If a man is 3 miles from the South Pole and if he walks in a straight line to the South Pole and then straight on, he is now going north and will finish up 5 miles from his starting point.

Answer No. 48

UQ.7   Give the Difference Between Two Unknowns

B: This is an unprincipled trap. The answer is 0. In any large sample, the differences will be the positive and negative in equal proportions, so that they will cancel out and lead to a result very close to zero. In the other case we followed the normal usage and that "the difference between" meant that we take the smaller from the larger number.

Note: One *could* argue that these tests performed on an actual sample of random numbers would be a test of the randomness of the series. If in any large set the averages differed greatly from the above, it might be claimed that this was not a random set. However, to befuddle things still further, we may resort to the delightfully torturing argument that, in any infinite series of truly random numbers, there must occur sub-sets with every degree of deviation from the mean. And then, always adding more confusion, we can argue that the probability that we should ourselves encounter such a deviant set of any great length is so low as to be negligible and that in our life on this earth it does not pay to take into account probabilities which are negligible, and so on and so on and so on.

Answer No. 49

T.7   Telling the Time with a Trombone

A: The most correct answer is that the interval is $\frac{12}{11}$ of an hour, or to put it in decimal terms 1 hr. 5 mins. 27.$\dot{2}\dot{7}$ seconds.

Answer No. 50

S.9   Answer: 15.

This is wickedly difficult. It is the result of adding the series of descending prime numbers to the ascending series, 2, 4, 6, 8, 10, thus:

13	11	7	5	3	2	1
2	4	6	8	10	12	14
15	15	13	13	13	14	15

Answer No. 51

K.8   The Racist Ice Cream Vendor

The ice cream was horrible.

Answer No. 52

T.20   Getting Things Mixed Up

The word "Mairshops" is simply an anagram for aphorism, i.e. scrambled aphorisms.

A: Science bends; dogma breaks.
B: Condemn prejudice, pardon judgment.
C: Great minds think unlike.
D: All compassion is discrimination but not all discrimination is compassion.
E: Praise without discernment is one-handed clapping.
F: Praise improves performance, condemnation improves excuses.
G: Without intelligence freedom is bewilderment.
H: The dagger of malice has a sharp handle.
I: Everybody doing their own thing produces a lot of poor things.
J: To show that a statement is not disinterested is not to show that it is false.

Answer No. 53

K.9   I'll Show You My Operation, I'll Show You My Figure

The number or integer was 1,000 and the operation was to calculate its reciprocal, that is, to divide 1 by the number giving 0.001. If I now divide 1 by *that* I get 1,000 gain. Each even "reciprocalisation" gives me the original integer and each odd one the millionth part of it. 8 is, on the best authority, *even* and 9 is held with little contradiction, to be *odd*.

Answer No. 54

UQ.8   Pseudo Non-Randomness

The probability is 1, a certainty. Random numbers are hell. It might be argued that you cannot calculate the number with the information given. You want to know the *length* of the series. But you were told that it was part of the set of random numbers and this is infinite. In an infinite series of random numbers — wait for it — not only will this configuration occur but it will occur an infinite number of times, so the only possible answer is: The probability that the line of numbers is part of a set of random digits is 1.0.

Answer No. 55

T.7   Telling the Time with a Trombone
B: 6.32 and 43.63 seconds.

Answer No. 56

S.10   Answer: 0.0588.
Rule — these are the reciprocals of the prime numbers to the nearest four decimal places.

Answer No. 57

K.10   Gun Switch
Being a spy the man had a reversible coat. He had turned it inside out with the result that outside pockets became inside pockets and left-hand pockets became right-hand pockets.

Answer No. 58

T.19   Nine Digits Squared Away
A: These are a number of answers, for example,

$9 = 3^2$ $81 = 9^2$ $324 = 18^2$ $576 = 24^2$

$361 = 19^2$ $25 = 5^2$ $784 = 28^2$ $9 = 3^2$

$529 = 23^2$ $36 = 6^2$ $1 = 1^2$ $784 = 28^2$

Answer No. 59

UQ.9   The Odds? Evens!
It was an even number and the reasoning is as follows:
   Consider the number of "shaken-hands" (S.H.s). Every normal handshake involves two S.H.s. The number of S.H.s must be even because for every normal handshake between a couple there are two S.H.s. The total number of S.H.s produced by those who shook hands an even number of times is obviously an even number. Deduct this from the total of all S.H.s which we agreed was even and we must have an even number. If an odd number of persons shook hands an odd number of times, the number of S.H.s would have been odd which is a contradiction, so it must have been even. This establishes a very important truth which will change the course of history.

Answer No. 60

T.8 Four-Letter Words

The context is, "the Deity". The Greeks had a word, "tetragrammaton" (four letters), for the ineffable name of the supreme being of the Hebrews, YHVH, the Hebrew spelling of Jahveh, and in many languages the word for God has four letters. Dieu, Dios, Gott, Odin, Jove, Zeus, even in English a very usual form is Lord.

Answer No. 61

S.11 I Hope This Upsets You

Answer F. The series is — "1 stable, 2 unstable" figures repeated. F is the only stable lettered figure to follow 2 unstable ones.

Answer No. 62

S.24 Magic Cubes

Here is one answer giving the total 9 down, across and *through*.

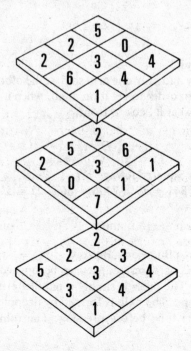

Answer No. 63
K.11 The Ups and Downs of High Rise
The man was a dwarf and could not reach above the 15th floor button.

Answer No. 64
T.9 Twisting My Word
The answer is NOON.

Answer No. 65
S.23 Cube of Cubes
Answer: B. There are three parameters of variation. Small/large, square/circle, black/white.

Answer No. 66
S.12 Concentrate!
Answer: C.

Answer No. 67
K.12 Double Fault?
The poor little boy had only one arm so that the other one was sewn up on the jersey. In order to get it on at all, when it was inside out, he would have to wear it back to front.

Answer No. 68
T.19 Nine Digits Squared Away
B: One example is $841 = 29^2$ $7396 = 86^2$ $25 = 5^2$

Answer No. 69
T.10 How to Put a Bulge on a Bottom
The dye is formed as described, it can be opened to release the finished earpiece. The press is simply a parallel prism conforming to the internal shape. The bulb is formed by dropping a small piece of rubber into the tube before pressing. The rubber expands to

form the bulb, resumes its shape and can be tipped from the formed earpiece. (Rubber can be deformed but it is not really compressible.)

Answer No. 70
K.17   Cubist? Diagonalist?
B: 12. Every surface will have been divided into two except the top and bottom surface but two new surfaces will have been created so the number is doubled from the original 6.

Answer No. 71
K.13   Two Right Handers
The father was going to do some work on his car. The gloves were rubber gloves and one of them was inside out. The father simply reversed it.

Answer No. 72
S.13   What Next?
Answer: Y is the 25th letter (5^2) P is the 16th letter (4^2) I is the 9th letter (3^2) D is the 4th letter (2^2) logically the next is 1^2 equals A.

Answer No. 73
T.19   Nine Digits Squared Away
C: $139,854,276 = 11,826^2$ = smallest.
$923,187,456 = 30,384^2$ = largest.

Answer No. 74
T.11   Concrete Without Shuttering
You use your labour force to dig a large circular trench, both wide and deep. You then round off the central cylinder so formed into a dome shape. You now fill the trench and cover the dome with concrete to a sufficient depth so that the top of your dome is sufficiently below ground level. You now have a large cylinder of

concrete containing a dome of earth. When it is set, you tunnel under the concrete and remove the earth. You can of course leave earth shuttering to make entrances for entry and ventilation. (See illustration.)

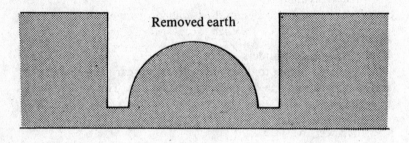

Removed earth

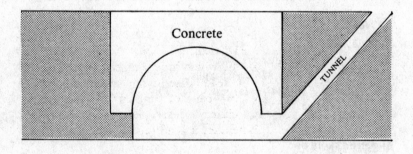

Concrete

TUNNEL

Answer No. 75

S.21   Ellipses and Squares
Answer: C.
Squares shrink downwards and rotate a quarter rightwards.
Ellipses grow downwards and rotate an eighth rightwards.

Answer No. 76

K.14   Brostles and Brongs
Brostles are four-faced pyramids, tetrahedrons, and its brongs are its corners or vertices.   When I cut off a brong, I create a pentrahedron with six vertices and also another tetrahedron (a brostle) with the normal four vertices (brongs).

Answer No. 77

S.14   Answer: A.
The groups of letters designate the number of straight or curved lines in the capital letters of the alphabet, A, B, C, D, E, F. The next letter, H, has three straight lines, and so should be designated SSS in this system.

Answer No. 78

T.18   Making Things More Difficult
There are two answers to this which must be used according to circumstances. If *you* say "a dead horse" *I* say "no, two pairs of trousers", and if *you* say "two pairs of trousers", I say, "no, a dead horse!" If you say "either a dead horse or two pairs of trousers," I say, "no, it is neither, it is a brace of pheasants" and so interminably on. . .

Answer No. 79

T.12   Cooked Books
A: $2 - 2 \div 2 + 2 \times 2 = 4$ and
     $2 \div 2 + 2 \times 2 - 2 = 4$

Answer No. 80

S.20   Senseless Shapes and Scattered Letters
Answer: D.
You should observe only the numbers of the letters and whether they are outside or inside. Interior letters are negative, exterior letters positive, and addition is to the right and downwards. The query square should contain nought as in the square lettered D. I shall be annoyed if you got it right because you were not supposed to!

Letters outside = plus   letters inside = minus

$$+2-3 = -1$$
$$-3+4 = +1$$
$$-1+1 = 0$$

Answer No. 81

S.12   Concentrate!
B:
8 (eight) in decimal counting or 1000 in binary counting.
  The figures represent binary counting with a circle meaning nought and a square meaning one. The digits are not arranged linearly but concentrically with the most significant digit to the outside.

Answer No. 82

S.15   Random Squiggles
Answer: C.
The order arises from the number of terminations, the line of diagrams has from 0 to 6 terminations and logically the next diagram must have 7, as C does.

Answer No. 83

K.15 The Hunters' Return

If there had been one hunter, the North Pole would have been a good answer. The three separated hunters could be at any three points a mile apart on the circumference of a circle of radius approximately $1 + \frac{1}{2\pi}$ miles with its centre at the *South* Pole. After walking one mile south, each proceed eastwards round a circle which is of 1 mile circumference so that he arrives back at the point where he touched that circle. The next leg, the one mile northwards march, will bring each hunter back to his starting point.

The real puzzle here, of course, is to explain what the Devil they thought they were up to. To this puzzle there is no answer!

K.15R Rosenthal's Variation

Postscript: One Mensa friend, Ernst Rosenthal, points out that there are many more answers and the new problem for you is at what other places — now you know the above — may the hunters stand?

See Answer No. 91.

Answer No. 84

T.12 Cooked Books

B: There are 16 recipes for cooking the books to give the answer 2, and here they are:

+	×	÷	—	—	+	÷	×
+	÷	×	—	—	+	×	÷
+	—	÷	×	—	÷	×	+
+	—	×	÷	—	×	÷	+
×	÷	—	+	+	—	÷	×
×	—	+	÷	+	—	×	÷
×	—	+	÷	+	÷	×	—
×	+	—	÷	+	×	÷	—

Answer No. 85

S.19   Another Dreadful Punzle

The eighth term is wrong, it should be 93

Starting point = —5 add 14 at each step but ignoring the numbers and noting the print form the elements form another series, coded in 3-base integers thus:

Small white digits   = 0
Small black digits   = 1
Large white digits   = 2

So the eighth term should be in 3-base 22 = 8 decimal, i.e. 9 and 3 in large white figures

Decimal	1	2	3	4	5	6	7	8	9	10	11	12
3-base	1	2	10	11	12	20	21	22	100	101	102	110
	—5	9	23	37	51	65	79	93	107	121	135	149

Answer No. 86

S.16   Cut That Out!

Answers: 24 and 25.

You will notice that some of the patterns are "undercut", that is, you would have to lift them out, you could not slide them out once they had been cut. The silly obsessive pattern he had arranged was "undercut, undercut, not-undercut, undercut, undercut, not-undercut . . ." 24 and 25 are two not-undercut patterns together.

Answer No. 87

K.16   Why Do the Gods Hate Kansas?

The distribution is about equal everywhere but the scientific interest in meteorites started in mountainous or post-glacial regions where natural earth-formed boulders are frequently found. In such country a stony meteorite is unremarkable and is often passed over. But iron boulders are rare and therefore noticeable. Isaac Asimov tells us that the earliest form of iron known to man was probably meteoric in origin. So in the flat boulderless plains of Kansas it is possible to make a true assessment of the intensity of a Heavenly Pelting because in that country even a stony meteorite is remarkable and gets into the count.

Answer No. 88

T.12 Cooked Books
C: There are only 5 dishes you may cook with these ingredients. 0, 1, 2, 3 and 4.
None of the 4 (= 24) ways give answers outside this range!

Answer No. 89

T.17 That Crafty Land Grabber, Ali
Question A: No.
The triangle could not be equilateral for reasons which will appear.
See Answer No. 93.

Answer No. 90

S.17 The Martinet
It is the 17th turn which is wrong. My instructions had been to march the squad to the pattern, right turn, left turn, left turn; right turn, left turn, left turn, and so on. 17 is the point where there are 2 right turns in succession, breaking the pattern.

Answer No. 91

K.15R Rosenthal's Variation
Yes! They may stand on any circle where the march south brings them to the perimeter of any circle concentric with the Pole which is $\frac{1}{n}$ miles in circumference, where n is any whole number.

Answer No. 92

T.13 All Bounce
Answer: 180 mph.
The iron plate on the train and the ball collide at a speed of 120 mph and the elastic deformation which occurs absorbs the energy of this collision. The energy imparted therefore forces the ball to

bounce back at this speed from the surface of the plate on the train. But the plate is itself moving at 60 mph so the total speed relative to the ground (the boy) will be three times the initial speed or 180 mph.

Answer No. 93

T.17   That Crafty Land Grabber, Ali
Question B: (See diagram opposite).
Ali was not a mathematician so he would be seeking a method using construction. The following was his method and anything on these lines would serve. Finding the centre of symmetry of the ellipse he drew a circle which touched it at the ends of its smaller axis. Knowing that an equilateral triangle is the one of greatest area that can be inscribed in a circle, he then marked any three points round the perimeter of the circle which designated an equilateral triangle. He now projects lines from the corners of this triangle, parallel with the long axis of the ellipse. The points where these projections cut the ellipse define a triangle which bears the same relation to the ellipse as the original triangle does to the circle. It is therefore equivalent to the one of greatest area that can be drawn. The shape of the triangle depends on his starting point. It would be isosceles if any of the sides were parallel with the major axes and scalene if these were not. It cannot be equilateral.

Answer No. 94

S.18   An Unforgivably Difficult Punzle
"LOve". The sentence carries a numerical message. It is counting from 1 in a binary code where capital letters = 1 and lower case letters = 0.
So the answer is LOve or any other four-letter word with the 3rd and 4th letters lower case which makes sense of the sentence.
This is the code:

Decimal	1	2	3	4	5	6	7	8	9	10	11	12
Binary	1	10	11	100	101	110	111	1000	1001	1010	1011	1100
Code	I	Do	GO	Off	AnD	YEs	YOU	Must	ParT	FrOm	ThIS	LOve

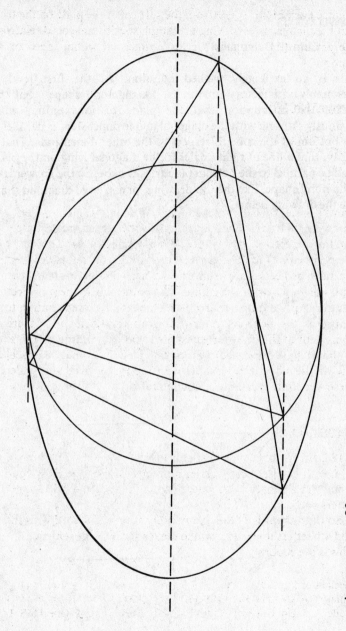

Answer to No 93

141

Answer No. 95

K.17   Cubist? Diagonalist?

A:

This is an extremely wicked question. At the first level, a reasonably satisfactory answer is "A diamond shape" but this makes the assumption that the plane of intersection, while obviously slanting with the diagonal in one dimension, is parallel to the bottom of the cube as respect to the other dimensions. That is to say, that a line at right angles to the diagonal lying on the plane shall be parallel to the bottom plane of the cube. So the answer is — a diamond shape, like the top drawing, or a skewed diamond shape like the drawing below.

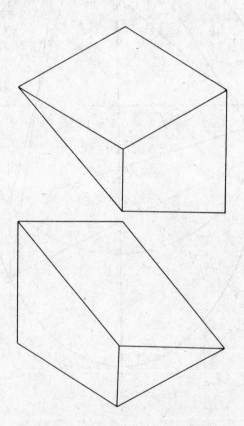

'SQUARE' DIAGONAL

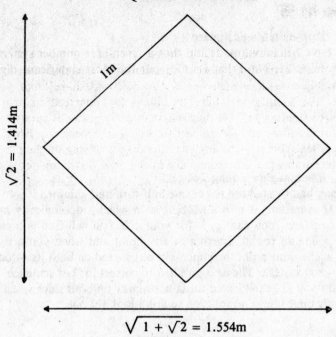

$\sqrt{2} = 1.414\text{m}$

1m

$\sqrt{1 + \sqrt{2}} = 1.554\text{m}$

'SKEWED' DIAGONALS

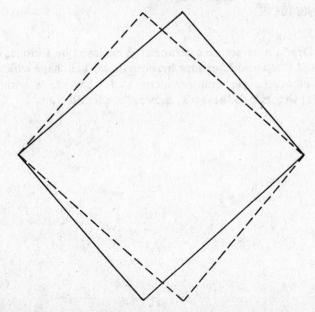

Answer No. 96

S.22   Brzöibian Magic Square
They have 7 manipulopods and thus a seven-base number system.
The total is 21. Note that Brzöibs put the most significant digit
below.

Answer No. 97

T.14   The Naughty Young Twister
The boy had twisted the paper one half turn and gummed it into a
ring, thus making it into a Möbius strip which, topologically has
only one face. You can try it for yourself. You will find you can
draw a line all round, starting at any point and when you arrive
back at the same point the paper will be covered on both its — one
side — so to speak. The next puzzle is to correct the last sentence —
how do you say the twisted torus has marks on both sides when it
has only one? I have no solution so don't look for one.

Answer No. 98

T.3   Klondyke
The largest area per unit perimeter is enclosed by a circle, circles
will not "nest" without gaps between them. The shape which gives
the most area per unit perimeter and which nests with other
similar shapes is the hexagon, as bees have found.

Brzöibian Magic Square

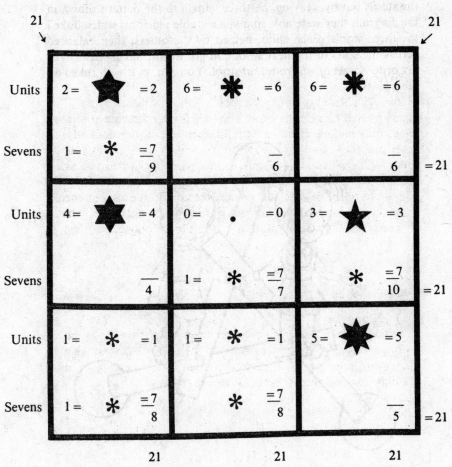

Answer No. 99

T.15 You Will Obey

One of them reached for the stilts and passed it around to the others. They were, of course, too short to bridge the gap between the stools but by weaving the three stilts into the pattern shown in the diagram they were able to make a stable platform which linked the three stools. Each child, helped by the others, then balanced across the stilts to the next stool and got down, having disobeyed my order to get down from *that* stool. You can try it with rulers on table glasses.

Answer No. 100

Three-Dimensional Noughts and Crosses
The best way to count without confusion is to count "centres" of possible lines and to see how many each centre has.
Thus:

Centre cube centres 13 lines	=	13
Each of 6 centres of face centre 4 lines	=	24
Each mid-edge centres 1 line	=	12
Total No. of lines		49

Feghoots

For those sad solvers who cannot see the original form of the distorted catch-phrases, I list them below:

Too many cooks spoil the broth.
A horse of another colour.
Many hands make light work.
Pot calling the kettle black.
Can't see the wood for the trees.
Pot calling the kettle black (Yes — again)
The Origin of the Species.

PART 2

MORE PROBLEMS, POSERS, PUZZLES AND PASTIMES

by VICTOR SEREBRIAKOFF
INTERNATIONAL CHAIRMAN OF MENSA

with the collaboration of
KENNETH RUSSELL
Puzzle Editor of the Magazine MENSA

The Problems

Kickself Problems

Kickself problems are those where you kick yourself when you hear the answer you should have known. They look impossible before, and obvious after you hear the solution.

Kickself Problems first afflicted the world at a lunch in Cambridge when Arthur C. Clarke asked Clive Sinclair and myself this, The World's First Kickself Problem.

'What was the first human artefact to break the sound barrier?'

I kicked my own ankle under the table when Clive paused briefly and gave the obvious-when-you-know-it answer, 'the whip'. The tip makes a tiny sonic boom with the crack, as it passes Mach 1.

They are vile, antisocial things, Kickself Problems. They have caused a lot of human shame, misery and injured ankles. They are published reguarly in *MENSA* the Mensa magazine. Look at the ankles of any Mensan. You will see the scars.

There will be plenty of Kickself Problems to aid to the General Horror of this book. You are advised to put your gaiters on now.

Here is the first one.

P1 Abracadabra

This is a magic word found in amulets, a nonsense word, a gibberish word, which was unfortunately found in a second century poem by Serenus Sammonicus. Ever since then it has been the conjurors way of saying 'Look how clever I am'. No one has ever said the word with a proper sense of humility. It is a nasty, clever-clever, self-satisfied, boastful word that we could well do without. It is a word I am quite sure that you wretched Frivolous Solvers will use repeatedly if I am unfortunate enough to have you solve these puzzles.

O.K. You are so clever. Tell me this then.

Even you, will see that starting with the top A in the triangular letter pile, there are several routes by which you can spell 'ABRACADABRA' downwards. I defy you to count them and get it correct. You are bound to get in a muddle and count one way twice or miss one or two. I say you cannot count them.

So! How many different ways of spelling ABRACA-DABRA can you trace?

```
            A
           B B
          R R R
         A A A A
        C C C C C
       A A A A A A
      D D D D D D D
     A A A A A A A A
    B B B B B B B B B
   R R R R R R R R R R
  A A A A A A A A A A A
```

See Answer No A1

P2 Every Which Way

Being a man of bounding energy himself, my Father always accused me of laziness. Perhaps I was lazy as a youth. But a really lazy man was my friend Tom.

I was lying in the sun by the river on a beautiful warm day. I smiled because I was feeling as happy as you would feel if you had just *solved* all these crooked, wicked puzzles. Tom stood by me looking as if he had just got the sack, found his car stolen and walked home through a thunderstorm to find his house burned down. He looked *miserable*.

I knew his problem and tried to help with good advice.

'If only you could pull yourself together and work up the

energy to ... lie down', I said.

You might not think that there are lazier and less lazy ways of writing but there are. Some scripts like Chinese go downwards, and so go upwards. Roman script goes from left to right, others go the other way.

The lazy scripts are ancient boustrophedon ones. The word comes from Greek, 'ox turning'. They go left then right like a plough. You read in both directions. The lazy writers were simply too idle to bring the arm back to start a new line. Diagonal scripts are unknown but I do not care, there are some here. In this wicked puzzle you cannot afford to be lazy because the words you are seeking are pan-directional: they read every which way.

The direction of each word is from each number to the following one whatever the direction. Each word after the first begins with the last letter of the previous word. The clues might help, or hinder. The bracketed number gives you the number of letters in case you are too idle to count them. Try it. Bad Luck!

Clues

1 Stiff fabric (9)
2 Shoulder piece (9)
3 Established (9)
4 Roman coin (8)
5 Able to be cut (8)
6 Interpret (7)
7 Crowded state (7)
8 Sail boat (5)
9 Success (7)
10 Pursued (7)
11 Obsolete (7)
12 Song for two (4)
13 Colour slightly (5)
14 Self esteem (3)
15 Eye (4)
16 Repetition of sound (4)
17 Egg (3)

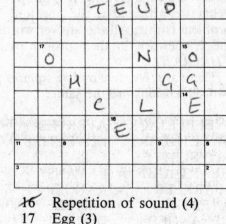

See Answer No A11

153

P3 Trilogical Acrossdownthroughword

Prose, ordinary writing, is monological, a linear string of signals that makes sense only in one-space. Crosswords are bilogical, they make sense in two-space, you can read them across and down, unlike a book.

It is not surprising that in all the years since the crossword first appeared there have been so few attempts to compose crosswords in three-space. The problem is that paper is two-space stuff which lends itself poorly to three-space presentations. Which is a challenge.

So! Here is a modest try at a 3D crossword, a Trilogical Acrossdownthroughword, which makes sense in three dimensions.

By wangling the threespace geometry we show all the little cubes that have to be filled with a letter (except two where the hidden cube is shown nearby).

The letters are *IN* the cubes, not on the faces (all six faces of a cube would show the same letter if it were not confusing).

We give you the empty crossword without clues. We even give you all the *ANSWERS,* all the words in the Trilogical. What we withhold is the position! Your childishly simple problem is this. All the answer words have to be fitted into the framework in their proper place, down, across, and *THROUGH*.

There are five, five by five squares where the five words in two dimensions are the same.

STEEPLEJACK	AVERTED	AGONE
SWEETHEART	NOVELTIES	AGONE
NOVELETTE		PANSY
HEARTACHE	PAVANS	PANSY
SPARKLER	RANGER	SEPTS
AVERTING	BANGLE	SEPTS
DERANGED	DECANT	PAVAN
ANGLERS	TOTEMS	TWIST
STEEPLES		
SERVICES	PAGAN	RULER
INTENSE	PAGAN	RULER

154

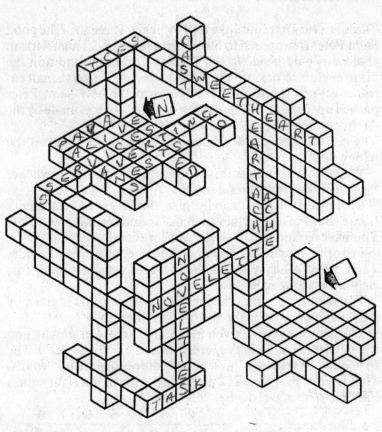

KNEEL	SPARK	~~VICES~~
KNEEL	EGRET	~~NESTS~~
PRONE	EGRET	~~NESTS~~
PRONE	AWOKE	~~TASK~~
~~ALIVE~~	AWOKE	~~SECT~~
~~ALIVE~~	SKELP	~~CAST~~
COVEN	SKELP	YAK
TIERS		
TIERS	YELPS	~~GO~~
ENNUI	YELPS	
ENNUI	TENSE	See Answer No A21

155

P4 It's Preposterous

There is a very impious joke told by pagan Russians. The good Saint Peter is supposed to have been a large jovial man with an enormous bald head. In the Russian Orthodox tradition the faithful have to pass up into Heaven through a very small entrance. When the Blessed Big Bonce of the holy Saint Peter pushed up through this tiny gateway a mistake was made by the Archangel Gabriel.

'Go back', cried the archangel, 'You are coming up the wrong way'.

Well that is also what this problem is, it is upside down, see the title (taken in its literal sense).

Crossword puzzles usually give the clues and an empty frame. But I give the clues both inside and outside the frame. You have to find the 16 words and list them.

I confine myself to one vowel, the one missing in the title. There are no other vowels in the 16 words you are looking for, eight across and eight down.

The number of times the missing vowel appears is given by the second number at the end of each line.

The consonants are given in the line, across or down. You will need them all, and they are muddled up, deliberately. The first number tells you how many you need. But not which. That is your job, that and arranging them in the right order. Find the sixteen words. Bet you cannot do it!

Clues
Across

1 'No Driving'
2 Unyielding to requests
3 Stupid 'Male'
4 Type of hat
5 Waterway
6 Accumulate
7 Substance that causes change
8 Fruit

(Handwritten answers):
WALKWAY 1
ADAMANT 2
JACKASS 3
PANAMA 4
CANAL 5
AMASS 6
CATALYST 7
BANANA 8

	1	2	3	4	5	6	7	8	
1	W	K	H	W	T	Y	L	T	52
2	T	N	S	M	T	Y	D	V	43
3	S	C	C	S	J	L	K		52
4	T	T	P	T	G	M	L	N	33
5	C	S	R	T	N	S	L	N	32
6	G	S	S	M	R	L	F	S	32
7	C	N	Y	T	M	L	S	T	62
8	N	B	S	K	M	D	F	N	33
	43	43	42	42	54	41	43	32	

156

1	Choral work CANTATA	5	Boat CATAMARAN
2	Card game CANASTA	6	Showing sorrow SADLY
3	Worry HARASS	7	Lucerne ALFALFA
4	Act harmfully ATTACK	8	Cease AVAST

See Answer No A31

P5 Animal Collections

Why we should talk of a herd of cattle but a flock of sheep escapes me. A collection is a collection is a collection. I make it a practice to talk of a swarm of goats, a herd of ants, gaggle of chickens, a crowd of bees and a flock of people. When people correct me I just say in an irritating way. 'I am so sorry you cannot understand me, I shall try to speak slowly and in a more orthodox way to help you'.

In the following list we have followed my principle of mixing things up for the hell of it. It is for you to take on the idiotic task of unscrambling the pairs. Which of the nouns in the left-hand list should go with the creatures in the right-hand list? And for Heaven's sake why?

STALK	of HUNTERS
BUILDING	of SWANS
CLOUD	of MAGPIES
SKULK	of FORESTERS
COVERT	of LAPWING
HERD	of BADGERS
CONVOCATION	of FRIARS
SORD	of COOTS
BLAST	of ROOKS
DESERT	of MALLARD
TIDING	of EAGLES
COLONY	of SEAFOWL
NIDE	of PHEASANT

See Answer No A41

P6 Improbable Sequences or Word Surgery

The surgeon was surprised when he found that the patient was a tradesman who called upon him daily.

He fought long and hard for the poor man's life, but 'lost him on the table'. Surgeons hate that. Shaking his head over the poor man's body he was fascinated by a very elaborate and beautiful tattoo on the skin from the abdomen that he had had to remove. He found it so rare and strange that he did not restore it to the body but put it in alcohol to preserve for the hospital's collection of medical curiosities.

He wrapped the bottle and took it home.

His wife had to cajole for some time before he would break medical etiquette and show her the contents of the mysterious parcel which so intrigued her. When she saw the strange memento she burst into tears.

'Oh! My God! Poor Jack Tomms our milkman is dead!'

This illustrates that the whole can sometimes, and I did say sometimes, be recognised from a part. That is why it is not quite hopeless to solve this word surgery problem. Merely nearly hopeless.

Word Surgeon Russell has been at work slicing bits out of some well known English words. These are the mementoes left after the butchery. Can you be as clever as the surgeon's perceptive wife? Each of these gory morsels has been amputated from an English word. What are the words? List them.

UFA   NXI   CYT   CKN   YRR   OOKKEE   WKW   YX

See Answer No A51

P7 Russell Square

When they are published in the Mensa Newsletter Ken Russell calls these Puzzles Magic Squares. But the Oxford Dictionary gives that name to number squares which add up to the same down across and diagonally. So since Ken is so adept at composing these I shall call them Russell Squares.

This Russell Square is made from the same six six-letter

words reading down and across. They are too easy, so the clues are muddled.

FIND THOU THE SIX WORDS AND WRITE THOU THEM DOWN

Answers are the same Across and Down. Clues are not in correct order.

Clues

Fireplaces   *INGLES*
One at a time   *SINGLY*
Polishing cloth
Secret meetings   *COVENS*
Help   *ASSIST*
Choose   *SELECT*

See Answer No A61

P8 Nursery Tales at my Mother's Knee

I was eight and beginning to feel my feet. I had not finished my meal.

'Eat up your nice shepherd's pie and greens', said my cockney Mum, 'there are millions of children in India that would go on bended knees for what you are leaving on your plate'.

I was a Very Nasty Little Boy. I said,

'Name three!'

There was a pause. Then my Beloved Mother gave me some advice which I have always remembered.

'Victor. If ever a strange man, one you have never seen before, comes up to you, offers you sweeties and asks you to go for a lovely ride in his nice motor car ... take the sweets and GO.

So there were no stories and nursery rhymes that night. But you My Dear Reader, shall have the benefit of the doubt. You may not be Very Nasty as I was. So you shall do better. You shall have a nice Nursery Rhyme Crossword. All the clues are in the Rhyme but you shall have no clue from me about where the words go. That you will have to sort out for yourself. I am still rather Nasty.

The Queen of Hearts who wore a piece of pure carbon crystallized in octahedron shapes, and who suffered from heart ailments, made some malleable flexible tarts filled with orange coloured stone-fruit jam, all on a Summers day.

The Knave of Hearts, of doubtful beginnings, who had discovered the correct sequence of the safe numbers, and who dislikes intensely a wife of a Duke, stole those tarts and took them clean away.

Complete the crossword, the eight clues are contained in the narrative above. Having solved them, place the answers in the correct positions.

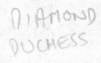

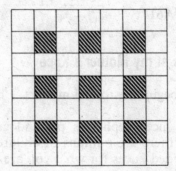

See Answer No A71

P9 The Labyrinth

Most people have a horror of being lost in a confined space, a labyrinth. And this is why you now have this labyrinth problem to solve.

Your people have sent you as a sacrifice to placate the Minotaur of Crete. Only if you can trace the right path through the labyrinth and find the sacred password can you escape and avoid joining the bull children, whose life is short and dreadful in the bull ring. The teasing Princess Ariadne has written a single letter of the password you seek in each of the fifteen rooms of the labyrinth. You may visit the rooms in any order but once you have entered each, it is closed to you. You may pass through the circumscribing corridor as much as you like. You must collect the letters in the right order.

Can you save yourself? What is the password and what is your path. Oddly, the password is a modern English word which makes it harder for an ancient Greek like you. Goodbye. I can only wish you a swift end from the First Bull.

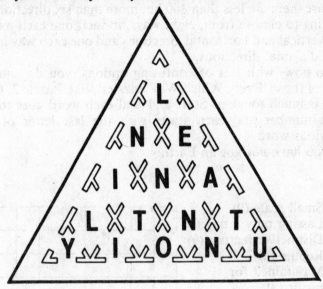

See Answer No A81

P10 Writing Two Pi Plus

People shout for freedom but most of them do not really like options.

I was once a carpenter's mate and we were repairing a window after a bomb during the war.

'Give us me bleedin' beadin' plane then.' The carpenter politely requested at one point.

I searched the tool bag and broke the news.

'I bin an' forgot it, unn'I?'

'Thick Sod! Nemine. I'll talk to 'er wun I?'

So he spoke to the lady of the house. Option cutting.

'What cha wan' 'ere Mum. A nice neat clean chamfer? Or a bloody great ugly bead?'

The lady considered the matter and made a creative, innovative decision in favour of a bead.

But there will be no such easy options for you.

There are three hundred and sixty degrees but only 2 Pi, a little over six, radians in the full circle. In this awkward square there are less than 360 but more than six directions of writing to choose from, eight ways, in fact, one each way in the vertical and horizontal directions and one each way in the two diagonal directions.

So now, with lots of confusing options, you do another one of those 'Every Which Way Puzzles', like Puzzle 2. Only this is much tougher. Start at 1 and each word goes to the next number and each starts with the last letter of the previous word.

You have not got an Earthly.

Clues

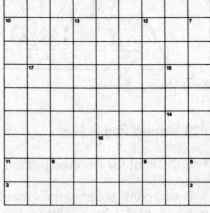

 1 Small scale (9)
 2 Lasting only a day (9)
 3 Distinctive feature (9)
 4 Reptile (8)
 5 Maintained for
    profit (8)
 6 Body armour (7)
 7 Daub (7)
 8 Nymph (5)
 9 Meanwhile (7)
10 Cosmetic (7)
11 Hangs on (7)
12 Layer (4)
13 Imitates (5)
14 Total (3)
15 Give out (4)
16 Fish (4)
17 Taste (3)

See Answer No A91

162

P11 Every Man His Own King

Mankind has not always had sit props. The first raised sitting place was a throne. The Chief, King, or Priest was elevated above The Rest to assert Mastery. He sat, honoured alone, on high, in state. In some tribes in Africa it is still only the Chief who may sit on a stool and wield the flywhisk that indicates idle mastery.

But all honours are cheapened with time and now anyone may vauntingly sit in a raised chair without elitist presumption. Nowadays we are all Esquires, (squire) or Mr. (master). Gilbert rightly wrote 'When Everybody's Somebody then No-one's Anybody.'

And seats, chairs, stools of all kinds have proliferated so we come to the problem of finding 12 different kinds of bum props in the list below. Fill in the spaces between the letters to make 12 words for sit things.

1 __H__O__E	7 __I__A__
2 BENCH	8 __T__O__A__
3 __U__B__E	9 __O__F__E
4 ARMCHAIR	10 __O__D__H
5 __R__C__I__I__M	11 __I__K__Y
6 SETTEE	12 __A__T__U__L

See Answer No A2

P12 Kickself Problem Class Consciousness

We think of class consciousness as 'being aware of social class'. But the very first activity of our Mind in the world is that of trying to be conscious of classes, trying to classify experiences.

This set is the different appearances of Mother's Face, this set that of Father's. Whenever Baby perceives a member of this set, Mother is here. Members of the other set of appearances tell Baby that Father is.

Taxonomy, seeking to be class conscious, finding out what classes of repetitive experience there are in the world, is the first act of mind. The first problem solving, the first display of intelligence.

There is an infinite number of ways of classifying any collection of entities. What Brain and Mind try to do is to find the useful ones, the ones that lead to valid predictions. Puzzles often concern Useless Classifications.

I have a modest example here, a set of capital letters from the Roman Alphabet.

S H O N I X ?

Where the question mark is, one of the letters from this set is missing. Your first Kickself Question is, which is it? Which letter should replace the query?

See Answer No A12

PART TWO (Not to be attempted until you have solved part one or more likely, looked up the answer). OK, satisfied? But do you really understand the principle even yet? I was fudging, I have smudged over something in the last answer. What was it?

Now look at this set.   B C D E I K O X ?

Whis is the missing Capital Letter which should replace the query?

See Answer No A50/B

PART THREE And by now you ought to be able to complete this.

A X I M O U V W H Y ?

Which letter should replace the query here?

See Answer No A60/B

P13 The Yonklowvitz Diamond

Mrs Yonklowvitz was having tea with a lady she had

met at the sumptuous hotel on the Miami beach. On her finger there was a ring. Such a ring! On the ring was a diamond. Such a diamond! It was not as big as a hen's egg. Well, not a large one, but it was big and very good and clear and white and glittery.

Her new friend Mrs Weinstein tried to be polite and ignore the ring but she could not do it. It obtruded. It insisted on itself. After a sherry or two and three creamy cakes she spoke.

'Such a ring! Mrs Yonklowvitz. Real diamond I can tell. Weinstein is the business. What a diamond! Over such a diamond I can't get. I should have such a diamond.'

'It is good-enough diamond. People notice it. Your man in the business and you ain't heard of the Yonklowvitz Diamond? They talk about it. In the world the biggest it ain't. Most expensive maybe, biggest in the world not. But in America! Well! Perhaps maybe some lady got a bigger one somewhere. If Yonklowvitz don't know about it.'

'A very lucky lady it is that you are to have such a diamond.'

'Lucky! schmucky! With everything good, God sends something bad. Sure I got the Yonklowvitz Diamond but I got a Big Disadvantage too.'

'So what is the Big Disadvantage Mrs Yonklowvitz?

'Yonklowvitz!'

Which brings us to rings. To tori. Well toruses. And the BIG PROBLEM.

Topologically a disc with a hole in it is a torus. So is a motor car tyre.

How good is your three dimensional imagination, your ability to manipulate in threespace? This is your problem.

Take a hollow torus such as an ordinary car tyre. Cut out the round attachment by which the air tube is attached to it. You now have a hollow torus with a small hole in it.

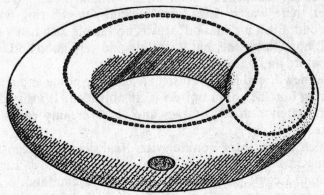

A) Could you pull the whole thing inside out through the small hole? (assuming it will stretch enough).

B) If you could, what would be the shape of the object after you had done it?

C) You will notice the bands which have been added to the hollow torus. There is a band which is affixed to the wall of the torus inside and which goes right round it the longest way. It is endless. Another endless band goes round *outside* the torus the shortest way. The two endless bands are of course interlinked and cannot be unlinked without cutting one of them. Your third question is, how will these appear when the torus has been pulled out through the small hole?

See Answer No A22

P14 Rabbits and Elephants

The circus had come to the little town and little Freddie ran out into the street to see the animals pass by. Imagine the mixture of joy, thrill, delight and envy when he saw his own friend Joey actually in the procession, leading three tethered elephants with a chain.

'Coo! Wedja get them big arimals?'

'Got myself a job wiva circus dinni? I gotta lead these to the Common, unni?'

'Wot are they? I like 'em'.

166

'They are called elephants, they got trunks on 'em'.
'Dun'alf like em. Can I 'ave one?'
'Nope'.
'Why not? Gimme one. Please'.
'Can't'.
'Why not?'
'They're counted'.

Here is a Kickself Question.

The Mummy and the Daddy rabbit were crossing the dangerous Road with the Little Rabbit, their bunny. They were nearly across when A Great Big Lorry thundered by right on top of them. Daddy Rabbit just managed to pull the other two to safety between the wheels as the lorry passed on.

The Little Bunny said, 'Whew! Daddy! That was a narrow escape for the two of us wasn't it?'

The Kickself question is: Why did the Little Bunny say 'two' when all three were safe?

The Kickself answer is he was only a Very Little Bunny Rabbit and he could not count.

Here is a simple enough matter. Can YOU count? I say not. All you have to do to prove me wrong is to count the squares in the diagram. Anyone can count things when they are all alike. These are all squares but the simple difference in the sizes is going to put you right off.

How many squares are there in the diagram? 19, 20, 21, 22 or 23?

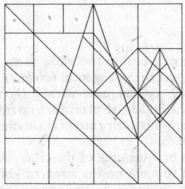

See Answer No A32

P15 The Long Arm of Coincidence

There is a problem about coincidences. The human mind is ever on the alert for the unlikely, it is unperceptive and dismissive of the usual. that makes sense for any animal. We have avoided the dangers and realised the promises of what we know about. The unusual presents new threats, new promises and these demand our attention. So the unusual makes a stronger impression on the mind and we tend to exaggerate its importance.

You go to a Mensa party and you are introduced to a lovely stranger. You find that her birthday is the same yours. Is that a coincidence? You must have met thousands of strangers in your life. It would be a coincidence if there were not several common birthdays. Yet you would both say. 'Isn't it strange', and feel a bond.

So here is the problem. How likely is a birthday coincidence? There you are at a little Mensa party. It is your first meeting and you know none of the other 23 people yet. You discuss this very problem. Someone is ready to bet you that there are no two people at the party with the same birthday. But they will only offer even money. Are the odds fair or is this a sharp Mensan trying to catch you? What are the odds?

See Answer No A42

P16 Graffitti

The local Authority put up two walls in an urban centre in modern Britain and the young local residents were faced with a problem. With typical bureaucratic thoughtlessness the local authority had made no plans for graffiti. The poor kids had to cover the walls with graffiti themselves so as to keep up local standards.

One wall was half the area of the other. A gang of public spirited lads set to work on the large wall but split into two gangs half way through the first day. The first half just managed to finish the large wall that day. The other half took on the smaller wall but could not quite finish before dark. All but one had to report to the Job Centre next day and there was only one lad left to finish the small wall. It took him all day before the last square metre was nicely covered and all was as it should be.

That was their problem. What is your problem? The young men worked with equal skill and at the same pace. How many lads were there in the gang?

See Answer No A52

P17 The Coefficient of Expansion of Zilch?

The coefficient of linear expansion of any substance is, as all schoolchildren but few adults other than some heating engineers know, is found by dividing the increase in length of a solid object by the product of the orginal length and the rise in temperature in degrees which caused that increase. For steel it is 0.00012 per degree centigrade. For other substances the coefficient is different. But what is the coefficient of expansion of zilch, of nothing whatsoever?

Let me give an instance to make the question precise. There is a disc of steel, one metre in diameter. At its centre there is bored a small hole as though the thing were an oversize gramophone record. The diameter of the hole is 10 mm. The disc is in a vacuum. The temperature of the steel is raised 10 degrees C. Never mind about the diameter of the disc. What about the hole? Is it smaller, larger or what? What is the diameter of the hole after the disc is heated?

See Answer No A62

P18 Kickself Calendice

Some calendars are big volumes of complex tables. The simplest calendar is a plain pair of Calendice as my portmanteau-word neologism would have it. Just a pair of numbered cubes. Twelve faces, yet you can show all the days of the month. But how? This is a Gaiters On question. You will need them if you do not spot how it is done.

There is only one digit on each face. I have even let you see some of them in the illustration. Your task is to say what digits are on the other four unseen faces of the left hand dice and the other three unseen faces of the right hand one. That is all. First it looks easy, then it will look impossible – until you make the lateral-thought breakthrough. Or miserably look it up.

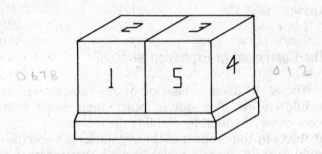

See Answer No A72

P19 Having the Balls to Take a Chance

Every nation has a neighbour nation against which it makes friendly stupidity jokes. Armenians laugh at thick Georgians and the Irish laugh affectionately at the stupid English.

Mensans grow tired of nationalist chauvinists who complain whenever anyone uses these joshing stereotypes to get a laugh in a miserable world. So they have invented 'the Densan' as the fall guy to make stupidity jokes possible. The Densan cap may be worn by an person or nation it fits.

THE DENSAN AND THE TYCOON
The golfing tycoon was showing off his new Rolls to his Densan aquaintance.
Densan And what is this for?
Tycoon It is a little car bar. I press the button, Presto! You can have a drink.
Densan Wonderful! And what is this button for?

170

Tycoon	I press that and it locks all the doors.
Densan	And what are these little spiked cups by your golf sticks?
Tycoon	Ah! I put my balls in those before I drive off at the green.
Densan	They do think of everything for your comfort, don't they?

This question is another one where you will need to have the balls to take chances, black and white ones in this case.

There is a covered box with a hand hole used by British clubs when selecting or rejecting members. Committee members can conceal the vetoing black ball in their hand and put it in unseen. White balls are 'yes' balls. If there is one black ball in the box when the Chairman opens it, the candidate/member is 'blackballed'. He or she is barred/evicted.

You have applied to a puzzler's club and the colour of the ball I put into the box depends on your answers to this.

In another blackball box there are 20 white balls and 30 black ones.

You take out two balls one after the other.

To avoid my blackball, you have to calculate these odds.

What are the chances of selecting these ball colours on separate trials.

a) Black then white? b) White then black? c) Two white? d) Two black?

See Answer No A82

P20 Bird Bush Tree

It has been established that a bird in the hand is worth two in the bush. But people who brave our fields with only a shotgun to protect them from the birds have an experience which I must report. They say that with ill-trained, hyperactive and hungry bird dogs it turns out that even a bird in the bush is worth two in the hound. And a bird in the hand must be worth three in the tree. The wretched things hide there.

171

And here we have both birds and trees hiding in sentences. It is your job to sniff them out. And kill the birds. And fell the trees of course.

There is both a bird and a tree in each of these sentences. And there is also an odd bird about. Find them and destroy them!

1) SHE HAS BEEN A WONDERFUL MARE BUT IT IS TIME SHE WAS PENSIONED OFF.

2) THE BIRD FLOUNCED AROUND BEFORE MAKING ANOTHER ONSLAUGHT.

3) THERE IS A TOWEL MISSING WHICH OUGHT TO BE REPLACED.

See Answer No A92

P21 A Bit Out of the Middle

You will hate this one, how you will hate it. Ken has been at it again. Word surgery now. He has operated on some siamese twins among words, hyphenated ones among the others. Why? Just to make it difficult.

Here are sets of adjacent letters from seven English words, and to be really nasty, three foreign ones that you ought to know but almost certainly do not. Some are hyphenated. There are bits out of the middle. But which words or hyphenated pairs?

| HANH | RESSW | LLSC | CHYD | RAFA |
| CKFR | NGGL | GOPHO | ICICO | ZZOR |

See Answer No A3

P22 Hard Words

I was a Small, Cocky, Nasty Boy in the front row at speaker's Corner in Hyde Park and I made a mistake. The speaker was in fine vein and had his large crowd enthralled.

172

'You people talk about socialism. You do not know the meaning of the word. There's a 'undred of you 'ere. I bet there is not one of you who can tell me what socialism is. Now then, I challenge you, anyone, What is the meaning of the word socialism. Just define it.' He paused. 'You see you can't can you?'

'I can define it,' I said.

'Oh! I see, this 'ere little lad thinks he knows so much better than all the rest of you. O.K. Sonny, tell me now what is *YOUR* definition of Socialism then?' He stilled the laughter. 'Nah then listen to 'im.'

I spoke up in a clear cheeky treble.

'Well Sir! The short definition of the word socialism is The National Ownership Of The Means Of Production, Distribution and Exchange.'

The speaker paused. then he delivered the following Hard Words.

'Look young man. It is one of the most 'orrible tragedies of this un'appy world that any child like you should be born. And even if you were, mercifully, to drop dead 'ere on the spot, the universal outburst of joy at your passing would be marred by the ghastly thought that you had already cumbered the Earth for so long. And even if the 'Eavens 'ad been kind and you'd never been born at all, the 'orrible thought that one day you *MIGHT* be born is enough to wake anyone screaming with 'orror in the night.'

The next puzzle concerns some hard words in another sense that you have to uncover. Reluctantly, we give you 12 clues. The words are in the jumble of letters in the grid. We have been wet enough to give an example even. The words are hard words. Very unusual. There are 12. Find them.

The answers will be found in the grid, the letters in sequence. Each letter to be used only once.

Example No 1 JOCUND
Clues

1 Merry
2 Duty on goods
3 Herbicide
4. Of a branch
5 Habitually climbing
6 Buddhist monk
7 Group of 4
8 Deformity of the foot
9 Infusion of dried herbs
10 Sword shaped
11 Metallic element
12 Gentle wind

O	R	Ⓙ	P	S	T	V	T	T
X	A	C	Y	I	C	E	T	A
T	I	R	A	Ⓞ	A	Z	A	E
T	P	L	A	S	A	T	N	P
R	M	Ⓒ	H	S	H	Y	R	L
R	O	P	O	U	R	G	O	Ⓤ
I	A	A	A	U	I	R	D	L
A	Ⓝ	O	I	S	A	N	T	U
D	I	L	R	N	I	M	E	Ⓓ

See Answer No A13

P23 Hey! C'Mon! Let's Get it Together, Man!

And now, my puzzled, head-scratching reader, it falls to you to make a considered, discriminating, apt choice among options. Your task is to assemble words which are Right and Good. And that is not all. From the lists below, you must complete 12 triplets, and that will be ruined by hasty ill-considered associations. Take a word from each of the three lists, A, B and C, and join them to make another word. Each word must be used but once.

A	B	C
THE	DID	GALE
INTER	OUR	AX
MAR	MAN	TICAL
CHIN	HE	AS
PAN	SON	NESS
STRAIGHT	TO	ION
WORK	FORWARD	ANT
DISC	SECT	MIME
PAR	ORE	AGE
CON	TIN	RING
WIT	ALL	ATE
CAN	CHILL	SHIP

See Answer No A23

174

P24 The Odds On Aces

I suppose we could best define a Miracle as an Event Against Which The Odds Are Infinite. For example, the odds against a better hand than five aces in a poker game are infinite, the probability zero, and easy to calculate. But let us come down to a more difficult problem and tackle the Paradox of the Second Ace.

We are playing bridge. I deal, and you say, 'I have an ace.' The odds against you having a second one can be calculated. They are 5359/14498. The probability $p = 0.369637$, less than 0.5.

But suppose we pick one ace, the Ace of Spades. I deal until you have this one. Now, what are the odds that you have another ace? Careful now.

See Answer No A33

P25 In the Proper Order

Precedences should be observed, things should be in the proper order, and this means getting priorities right.

A small aeroplane is on fire in flight. The cowardly pilot has jumped. Four people have to decide priorities because there are only three parachutes. The first passenger said, 'I am essential to my large business which will go under without me, causing mass unemployment. My aged parents depend on me and my fiancée is pregnant. I must live to make my child legitimate by marrying her.' There was no protest. He took a parachute and leapt out.

'I am young but I am of great ability. I am a Mensa member and I have been assessed as the most intelligent man on Earth. The world must not be deprived of my gifts.'

Without the consent of the others the young man shrugged his way into to the loops, buckled himself in and leapt out of the plane.

The third, a boy scout, began to buckle the parachute on to the old man who was left with him.

'No! No! lad, I am an old man, I have had a good life. You

are young and have the world before you. You take the last
'chute.'

'No problem Uncle! There are two 'chutes left, the Most
Intelligent Man in the World has just jumped with my
rucksack on.'

Order, priority. Which brings us, with strained relevance,
to series, ordered progressions.

What can you make of these series? What is the next term
in each case?

1)   F T F T T T T F F F F S S S S E E

2)   E O E R E X N T E N N E
      Does 11 go above or below the line?

3) $\dfrac{12 \quad 6 \quad 10}{345 \quad 789}$

See Answer No A43

P26 Odd One Out

The 21 seven letter words can be paired up into 10 pairs, find
the odd word which cannot be paired.

ANDVARI	HAUTBOY	NONAGON
BASLARD	HUMERUS	OCTAGON
BRASSIE	JUPITER	POCHARD
BUBALUS	NACARAT	PONIARD
BUFFALO	NEGRITO	SCAPULA
CASSINO	NEPTUNE	VIOLONE
DUNNISH	NIBLICK	WIDGEON

See Answer No A53

P27 How Many Books Make a Library?

When I was ill the International Board of Directors of Mensa
sent this cable. MR PRESIDENT. MOTION 24 PASSED
BY MAJORITY 9 TO 7 STOP I.B.D. WISHES YOU
SPEEDY RECOVERY.

176

I got to be so popular by asking amusing riddles and jolly jesting quizzes.

Let me give an instance. 'How many books make a library?' I ask. No one will pick on a figure. So I ask if one book is a library, two, three, four. Eventually, bored to tears, someone will agree that say, 30 books constitutes a library. Then I say 'You said that 29 books was not a library. Do you mean that a difference of one book makes it a library?'

I have a library and it has more books in it than the number of words in any book. No two books have the same number of words. From this scanty information you have to tell me the number of words in one of the books. You can do it. But you do not know you can do it. I find cricketer's pads useful.

See Answer No A63

P28 The Nursery Crossword

The two little boys were discussing life.
   'How old are you then?'
   'I dunno.'
   'C'mon you must know how old you are.'
   'I dunno 'zackly. I'm either four or five.'
   'D'ya smoke cigars?'
   'No.'
   'D'ya smoke cigarettes?'
   'No.'
   'D'ya drink beer or spiritis?'
   'No.'
   'D'ya go out wiv girls?'
   'No.'
   'You're four.'

Despite the fact that it is only a Nursery Rhyme Puzzle the inexperienced child would have had difficulty with this. So will you.

This Disturbed Nursery Rhyme slightly conceals eight Childish Clues which must serve you to solve the crossword puzzle. Find the words that are cryptically indicated and fit them into the grid. If you can!

In one of her whalebone corsets, old Mother Hubbard went to the sideboard on the sheltered side of the car sheds, to get her brave, bighead, pugnosed, hound a bone. When she got there the cupboard was bare and the dog got none. So she conceived an aversion to the breeding of the numerous exact replicas of the long haired game dogs that had emptied it.

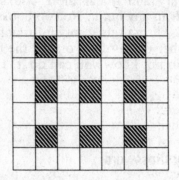

See Answer No A73

P29 Recognition Problem 1

Computers can do many things better than the human brain can. But there is one thing at which the human brain is still way in front, pattern recognition. I can recognise a friend's face, from any angle, in any light and when it is grossly changed by age or accident. I can even recognise the 10 scribbled lines of his caricature. I have seen Igor Aleksander's computer that can learn to distinguish a few faces but there is a long way to go to equal the brain.

Recognition has a lot to do with expectation.

Let me test your power of recognition under difficult circumstances. The topiarist wanted to communicate to passing hang gliders. As one does. He clipped his yews to the pattern shown. Being highly intelligent the hang glider pilots read his simple signal but can you? What was the topiarist trying to get across.

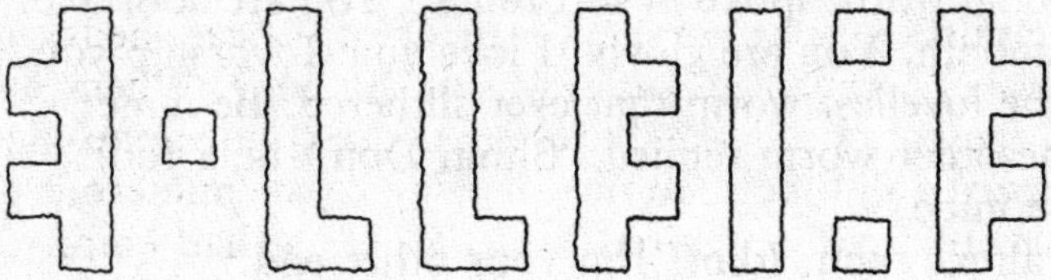

See Answer No A83

P30 Recognition Problem 2

A monk in Franciscan attire was in a railway carriage. Drinking canned beer and peeking at him in the corridor outside were several young gentlemen. There was not a couth youth among them. They guzzled and tittered until one opened the door of the carriage and asked the monk. 'And what are you supposed to be?'

'I am supposed to be polite. What are you supposed to be?'

What are things supposed to be? Recognition. If often depends upon the supposer. Or upon the supposers perception of what others might suppose.

In Beograd they use the Kyrillic alphabet and are a little less familiar with the Roman one. That may account for this inscription on a glass door that I saw there. It was written below the Kyrillic characters and was evidently intended to say something to Roman alphabeticists. But what? Can you decipher what it is supposed to be? You will kick yourself.

P H U ƨ L U L ꟼ

See Answer No A93

P31 Recognising Forms of Nothing

It was spring. The first fine day. The birds were far away. The worm felt bold, adventurous, masculine. It pushed its head up from its hole and saw the beautiful world outside. And there! Right at hand, the sweetest, dinkiest, pinkest, most beautiful little worm waving enticingly an inch away. The bold worm spoke in soft tones. 'You are adorable. You are smooth. You are glossy. I love you. I worship you. You are the loveliest worm that ever slithered. Be mine.'

The other worm replied. 'Shhh. Don't be a fool!'

'Be mine.'

'I already am. Idiot! I'm your other end.'

The recognition of self is vital and that is what the cells of your body have to do. Hence the science of immunology.

But how can you recognise nothing whatsoever.

That is what you have to do. Nothing has taken on many forms in the skeleton crossword. All the clues are the same. Nothing. Zero. Zilch. You have to solve the crossword in which every clue is nothing at all.

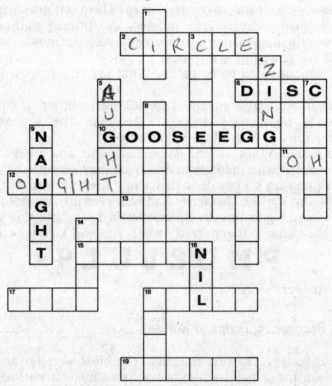

Clues Across			Clues Down		
2	0	(Geometry)	1	0	
6	0		3	0	(U.S.A. version of 7 down)
10	0	(Slang)	4	0	
11	0	(Exclamation)	5	0	(Variant of 12 across)
12	0	(Variant of 5 down)	7	0	(British variant of 3 down)
13	0	(Small one of 2 across)	8	0	
15	0	(Math)	9	0	(Math)
17	0	(Sport)	14	0	
18	0	(Slang)	16	0	
19	0	(Variant of 9 down)	18	0	

See Answer No A4

P32 Problem for an Impatient Lazy Man

It is said that the lazy intelligent man makes a good manager. He naturally thinks of economising man-hours which is often half the manager's task. But a manager must have a sense of urgency as well as laziness. Impatient men are needed, not procrastinators.

I was selling machinery in Moscow. My Russian contact just back from an Arab country was intelligent and lazy. But he had a great sense of urgency.

'Today,' he kept saying, 'must be done this signings today! "Bokhra" will be not O.K.'

After he had given me this, 'Today not Bokhra.' business several times I said, 'I do not know this word "Bokhra", what does it mean?'

'Apologisements. Is for me difficult. I mixing my speakings. "Bokhra" he is Arab word.'

'What does it mean?'

'For you English is not so easy to comprehending "Bokhra". Is best way explain I tell you it is same like Mexican word "Mañana", but not having same sense by urgency.'

Now a Kickself problem is an Impatient Lazy Man's Problem. The route to a solution seems long and troublesome and if you take it you never get there. There is a mental short cut somewhere. It is the Impatient Lazy Man that finds it.

A modest example follows.

There are 12,345 entries for The Mensa World Chess Knockout Competition. We do not count byes as games and draws are settled by tossing a coin. Now! How many matches have to be played to find the knockout winner. There is no calculation required. You should know the answer by now. But now!

See Answer No A14

P33 Blatant Alphabetic Discrimination

Dr Madsen Pirie wrote an article in the British Mensa newsletter *MENSA*. He complained about 'Alphabeticism' which he said was unfair to those whose names begin with letters which are late in the alphabet. There are many occasions in life he whinged, when people are served in alphabetical order.

After complaints against the injustice latent in alphabetic discrimination he proposed telephone directories with the names in random order.

Believe it or not a few Mensa members wrote to protest that the random directory idea was not really practical. Perhaps they were playing up to the satire but it did not sound like it.

Reacting to Madsen's daft plea we supply a crossword which uses all the 26 letters of the alphabet equally, each letter just once, *NOT IN ALPHABETICAL ORDER*. So without clues, you fill in the grid with dictionary words. There may be many solutions. The answer will give you at least one.

See Answer No A24

P34 Kickself Takeaway

This is a taking away problem. If taking away is overdone you have nothing left. An advantage sometimes.

Nothing is what you will feel like when you fail this test and see the answer.

Here is a list of letters. All you have to do is to strike out five letters and you should have a word which is in an English Dictionary. Pads on! It is a Kickself Problem.

A F P I O V E L L O E G T T I E R E S S

See Answer No A34

P35 Making Big Problems Out of Little Problems

Fourteen year old Petula looked worried when she came in from school: she ate no supper.

'Mummy! Daddy! I must talk to you,' she burst out.

Her kind parents stopped eating. They were all ears. Petula paused. 'I don't know how to begin. This is the time when I am going to need all your support. I've not told you about my boyfriend. I shall soon be fifteen and I am going to leave school and go and live with him so he can be a proper father to the baby that is coming. Please don't be cross Mummy, I know that neither of you has any racial prejudice and when you hear the whole story you will know that he was wrongfully convicted. He has promised me he is going to kick the habit anyway and then he is bound to get a job soon. He has a nice little room where we can stay.'

Mother wept. Father stormed. Petula ran up to her room.

A half hour later she came down and peeped round the door at her silent distressed parents.

'So sorry, Mum and Dad,' she said calmly, 'I've obviously overdone it. All I told you was a lot of rubbish. I just wanted to soften you up for some terrible news. I have completely failed on my O level exams.'

Which shows that sometimes it pays to make heavy weather, to exaggerate problems.

And that is exactly what we are doing here. The Hard Way.

The diagram shows a drawing roughly to scale of a large rectangle which is divided into 11 small squares (equal sides) in a complicated way. The dimensions are in whole metres, each is an exact square and they fill the whole of the large rectangle of which the dimensions are given. Your problem is to show the dimensions of the internal squares.

177 M

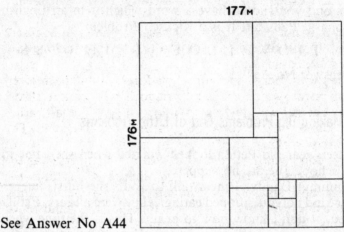

See Answer No A44

P36 Cubes and Double Cubes

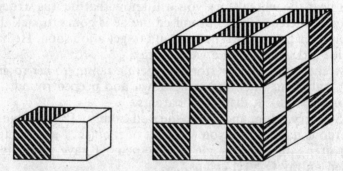

The large cube seems to be made of smaller ones but it was actually built up of 13 double cubes like that on the left, plus

184

just one single one. What colour must the single one be and where must it be put to build the large cube?

See Answer No A54

P37 Backseat Driving and D.I.Y.

It is my experience that backseat driving is endemic everywhere.

And it is not only drivers that suffer from the backseat adviser. If you take on any task with anyone watching you get unsolicited advice.

I dealt with such a one in my salad days. I had been given a cheap pocket watch which did not go. I was about to throw it away but as I was passing a flat lorry I gave it a last rather heavy knock on the lorry bottom and listened to it. The shopfitters working there noted my action.

'Why don't you try banging it with my hammer,' was the helpful suggestion of a grinning shopfitter. I took the hammer and smashed my watch up in front of their astonished eyes. Then I scraped together the handful of remnants, listened carefully to them and said, 'It still does not go. That was poor advice. You would do better to stick to your own trade.' And I walked on.

And here is another example and your problem.

Mr Doit Yussulf was covering a square table with square tiles when his friend Mr Bakseet Halpa called.

'Better to having smaller tiles, it looking nicer when you finish.'

'But I would need more tiles.'

'Not many,' Bakseet figured on his calculator. 'With three quarter inch smaller square tile you needing only 250 more tiles to covering table. It looking *MUCH* better.

'Screw,' said Doit as he continued his task, 'you.' And here comes the Nasty One. What size of tile was Mr Doit Yussulf using? And how many?

See Answer No A64

P38 Topological Nonsense Object

Object J is a solid object. It has no edges and only one face. What is Object J? Well, a sphere or an ovoid would do. But if either were hollow it would have two faces, one inside and one outside.

Now how about object K? Object K is solid, it is hollow, it has only one face and no edges and its inside is its outside and vice versa. When you pour liquid into it the liquid goes outside before it goes into it, though it still remains inside when it is outside. If you see what I mean. Do not blame me. Blame the man who invented the wretched thing.

What sort of thing is object K? Describe it or draw it. If you can.

See Answer No A74

P39 Romance and Tragedy

P39A The Slugs Adventurous Romance

There are these two lovely glossy silvery slugs. A mating pair, male and female, each leaving a brilliantly shining trail behind. I have put the male inside a hollow toroid form. Object S. It is quite frankly a very odd thing, Object S. The male slug is crawling along on the inside skin of the tube-like Object S. The tube is circular in section and toroid in form. I have put the female outside the wall of Object S exactly over her lover on the other side of the cruel glass.

The eager, seeking, adoring slugs crawl round the inner and outer walls of the tube and they do so continuously, never leaving the surface under them and never passing over any edge or indeed any discontinuity of any kind. The surface under them remains a smooth curve at all times. I have to be so specific because of the remarkable thing I am going to tell you next in this story of Love, Adventure and the Final Happiness of Two Simple Creatures.

The eager male starts on the inside wall with his loved one just through the glass on the outside but as they crawl they find a little later that their position has reversed. He is on the outside wall, she is on the inside one. Then as they crawl on this pattern constantly repeats. Always together, always divided by the spoilsport glass.

And so the wretched creatures go on, inside, then outside, each coming back over its own tracks. The poor, loving, yearning creatures become ever more desperate until the female loses hope and halts in a narrow place. Then Cupid smiled. The indefatigable male crawled on and three changes from inside to outside later he joined his sweet, glossy, slimy, overjoyed mate on the same side of the glass.

What can possibly account for all this? What is Object S like? What sort of torus are they crawling in and out of? You will earn a Lot of Chalks if you solve it because the shape you have to guess is not widely known and may be entirely new.

See Answer No A84

P39B The Slugs' Tragic Passionate Celibacy

In Puzzle 39A the two slugs finally got together and their love was requited, but now I have to tell a tragic story of unrequited love and tragic passionate celibacy. The circumstances were as before but the slugs were not put in Object S. Object X was their topological prison.

Object X was very much like Object S, the one-face hollow torus. It was different in only one small but vital way. Every word of the description of Object S applies and is just as true for Object X, the object into which they were put. As before, each was put on opposite sides of the glass wall at the same spot. The difference to the Loving Slugs was devastating. They slithered round the toruses trying to reach each other. But whatever they did they could not get to be the same side of the glass. As before each was alternatively inside and outside the object. But where he was outside she was inside and, painfully, vice versa. Even if she waited for him to come round he was always on the wrong side. There is no way they can meet without one of them passing over a discontinuity and that just is not allowed under the terms of the question.

If you have got the answer to P39A, you really should be

able to do this one now. What was the difference between Object X and the One-face Hollow Torus described as Object S in Puzzle P39A?

See Answer No A84

P40 He Rode Off In All Directions

Stephen Leacock described how the Gallant Knight mounted his trusty steed, doffed his vizor to his lady and rode off in all directions. And that is what you will have to do in this dreadful messy puzzle. It is unfortunately like those you have had before. You read from each number to the next higher and spell out the words to which clues are given. Each word starts with the last letter of the previous one.

Answers run from the lower number in direction towards the next higher number and after No. 1 the last letter of each answer becomes the first letter of the next.

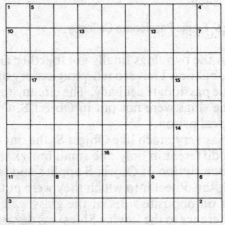

Clues

1	Utter powerlessness (9)	
2	Onlooker (9)	
3	Recoiling (9)	
4	Order of monks (8)	
5	Zigzag line (8)	
6	Inscribe (7)	
7	Of the intestines (7)	
8	Patch (5)	
9	List of customs (7)	

10 Free from deceit (7)
11 Animate (7)
12 Star (4)
13 Operatic songs (5)
14 Title (3)
15 Sea fish (4)
16 Chant (4)
17 Weapon (3)

See Answer No A94

188

P41 Kickself: Personholes

We have to change words for fear of being accused of sexism. But I hate 'Chairpersons' and the like. Sometimes you can do it by simply feminising the word. No one would object if you spoke of a Chairlady or cowgirl or milkwoman. But I am in difficulties with 'manholes' and have to go to the horrible 'personholes.'

What shape should a personhole be for safety. Why round, why not square or rectangular? I will tell you that it is thought round ones are safer. Why? That is your kickself question.

See Answer No A5

P42 The Message

Here is an odd message. Can you arrange the following 33 letters to make sense?

$$
\begin{array}{rcl}
1 & - & B \\
1 & - & C \\
1 & - & G \\
1 & - & H \\
3 & - & L \\
1 & - & M \\
3 & - & P \\
3 & - & R \\
5 & - & S \\
3 & - & T \\
11 & - & Y
\end{array}
$$

See Answer No A15

P43 Operation Hara Kiri

The Hara Kiri or Middle Chop, the Japanese form of suicide is a severe Test of Will. It is evidently meant to be. No sissy gas oven or car exhaust stuff for those people. You really have to Want To Go to go in for Middle Chop.

And this next Puzzle is a blatant Middle Chop Puzzle of the Worst Possible Type.

What Ken Russell has done is to collect 10 otherwise decent dictionary words, some of them hyphenated, which have committed Hara Kiri, slashed out their bellies with the drastic Middle Chop surgery.

Now Ken could have shown us the corpses of the words but he has chosen a more grisly course. He has displayed below, the chopped-out remnants.

It is from these fragments that you have to recognise and name the suicides, the words that have lost their guts. Remember some of the words were siamese twins, hyphenated.

OWGO	KEDW
GGLET	CHPU
BLESK	TTOG
EHOY	NNYP
EENN	NSSH

See Answer No A25

P44 A Sixer Russell Square

You have the easy job. Solving a Russell Square is child's play compared with composing one. And a six letter one is really tough. The same six words down and across. It's a doddle. No wonder we put the clues in random order. Let us see what kind of a mess you make of it.

Clues

Flower
Retreat
Trigonometrical ratio
Come to notice
Stage plays
Of smallest particles

See Answer No A35

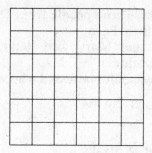

P45 Gather Ye Mensans While Ye May

Mensans do not meet. They gather. Mensa Founder Roland Berrill decreed 'We all sleep under one roof on the first Saturday in November each year.' And we do. He called it the Annual Gathering. We gather annually in many lands now.

This problem is a puzzling business about a Mensa Gathering which was set by a previous Puzzle editor, the barrister John Causer.

He could have simply told you the facts but he has been oblique, evasive and circumspect. You will have to deduce them.

If you can. Here is the tale.

Mensa Gathering
Five speakers at a Mensa gathering were housed in adjoining rooms at the Nottingham Hilton. They were busily preparing their talks.

Harold was making a paper pyramid to demonstrate its power to sharpen razor blades and clean the spark plugs on his Porsche. The astrology couple from Belfast, both Pisces, arrived and parked their Rover in the reserved space next to the BMW. Dorothy, in the room next to the end, said to her neighbour 'Joe and I used to live in Manchester before you moved there'. Kay admired the Mercedes owned by the couple from Fort William. He was the one with the red beard. Judy's husband discovered that he had left his paper on bisexuality at home in Truro. Fred, in 201, said to Ann

191

next door 'Those people from Derby next to you have a flat tyre on their Ford.'

Eddie and Mary were busy rehearsing their telepathy demonstration.

Who was Bill's wife and who was the speaker on hypnosis?

See Answer No A45

P46 Chance Breaks

What are the chances that a bone with a double fracture will make up a triangle?

Take out some convenient bone, the radius or ulna from your arm for instance. If you are fussy about it you can use a bone from someone else's leg. Choose two random distances from one end and break the bone at both spots.

Now. What is the probability that you can fit the three pieces together to make a triangle?

You ought to be able to do this without boning it up. Come now!

See Answer No A55

P47 Pawnees and Queenies

A Knockout Chess Competition detracts from the Sum Of Human Happiness because as we discovered in Puzzle P32 there has to be $n - 1$ losers and only one winner in n games. Golfers have partly overcome this problem by handicapping. I propose a simple ranking system for chess players too. There are Queenie players at the top of the heap going right down to humble pawnees at the grovelling bottom. There are a number of moves set between each rank. A Queenie has to beat a Rooky in 50 moves but must mate a Knighty in 40 and a pawnee in 10. Or something like that. Do not trouble me with details. If the high rank player needs more moves then the lower rank player has won. This would do away with the unfair advantages coming from study of the game, practice and higher intelligence and move us all towards a Just And

Fair Society. The idea of No-Win Games does not go far enough, we need Weaker-Wins Games.

Which brings me to your problem.

A Knighty player foolishly bet that he could win two games out of three against alternately stronger and weaker players. The sharp Mensan who took the bet managed to get him to accept an additional condition that he must win two games in succession. The artful Mensan then gave him two alternatives. He could play:

1) weaker—stronger—weaker

or

2) stronger—weaker—stronger

He outwitted the Mensan by making the optimum choice. What was it? Which did he choose? 1) or 2). Much more important (in a binary choice question). Why?

See Answer No A65

P48 Kickself Problem for Daily Amputees

I get interviewed a lot on the radio and television and one of the questions I am asked is. 'Why did you grow a beard?' I have stock replies to stock questions and the reply is, 'I didn't do anything.'

Is it not extraordinary that most men decide on a facial hair length which is impractically short. They have to cut it once, even twice a day to keep up to the absurdly high standard. If I had shaved, I would have lost over a year's work in the fifty five years since my beard came. Fifty eight forty hour weeks of continuous shaving it would have taken, no holidays. (I allow seven minutes a day for these multiple amputations of parts of the living body).

Barbers have created a strange market. Here is an odd Kickself question about them.

In the Schwabian town of Ulm in 1643 the Authorised Town Barber had managed to persuade the Mayor to pass ordinances that no man should have a beard, nor shave himself, and that only the Authorised Town Barber might shave anyone. The Authorised Town Barber was a resident of Ulm and bound by the law. Who shaved the barber?

See Answer No A75

P49 The Chance of a Deal

I can understand people playing some card games but not others. The whole family of intense silent games like Whist and Bridge are mum, glum, miserable, grouchy and unsocial affairs. Even between games there is nothing but quarrelling. They are against the whole sense of a social get-together when people sit for fun round a table. Poker, Brag, Pontoon, even Snap I can see the point in. They can be uproarious, jolly, shouting, joshing, legpulling, beer and laughter affairs. So what if the cards get dog-eared and soggy!

Here are some nasty, calculating questions such as thin lipped, puritan, odds-calculating Bridge players might ask.

You name a suit and bet on it.

The dealer deals just two cards from a shuffled pack. What are the odds that one of the cards dealt will be of the named suit? Do they favour you or the dealer or are they even?

See Answer No A85

P50 Order! Order!

You have 52 cards marked one to 52. If you deal the first four cards, what are the chances that they are in order of ascendency.

Eg. 1.   11—19—32—46
Eg. 2.   4—17—27—47 etc?

See Answer No A95

P51 Snap!

Two players shuffle a pack of cards each, and they deal simultaneously as in Snap. What are the chances that they will both lay down the same card at the same point in the deal, a snap deal in fact. What are the odds in the dealing of the whole pack?

See Answer No A6

P52 Two of a Kind

A dealer deals 10 cards face down. Five red cards and five black cards mixed up. You have to select a pair of red or black cards. Do the odds favour: The dealer, favour you, or are they exactly even?

See Answer No A16

P53 Pulling Stars to Pieces

Lots of boozers have excuses for drinking but my Russian grandfather drank to a system of excuses. For every ordinal drink a Planned Excuse.

'Is in Heaven only *ONE GOD.*' First vodka.

'HANDS on a man add to a *PAIR!* Second vodka.

'A *HOLY* "Two" was it? Or was it a *TRINITY?*' Slup!

'Round it, has a *TABLE, FOUR* legs.' Gulp!

'Points on it, a *STAR* counts *FIVE!*' Swultch!

By the time he got to the fourteen apostles he was in a mood to dissect stars.

Which is your next modest, simple task. Please pay close attention.

Here are three Baby Stars and a Bigger Star. You have to cut the Baby Stars up in such a way that the pieces will fit together exactly to constitute the Biggie Star. Each Baby Star has to be divided into four parts, three kinds, and then the dissected parts of the Baby Stars assembled to make up the Biggie Star.

And the best of Russo-British luck!

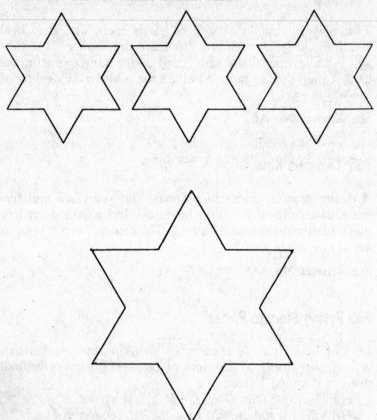

See Answer No A26

P54 Twin Kickself Problems

The terrified mother cuddled her nursling and screamed from the third floor window as the flames behind her licked closer.

The fireman shouted, 'First throw the baby down! Patrick will catch it.'

'No! No! He will miss it!'

'Throw the baby down! Patrick never misses. He is the best catcher in the world. He plays for Densan United the

Rugby team. Throw it down! It is the only chance.'

Patrick was a marvellous catcher but the mother was not a good thrower. Patrick had to run like a hare before he could scoop up the baby in the last foot of its descent. There was a great cheer from the crowd as Patrick recovered his balance. It died in their throats as Patrick booted the baby over the house.

A very nasty story. Now a pair of very nasty twin problems.

1) A woman has just three children. Half of her children are boys! Explain how that can be.

2) Another woman has two sons. They are born within an hour of each other on the same day, they are indistinguishable in appearance being uniovular. They are not twins. Explain that.

There is a perfectly simple explanation. Have you some plaster ready for your ankle?

See Answer No A36

P55 A Respectful Motionless Golfer

How can a man give offence simply by standing motionless? It can be done. And it was condemned. But was the condemnation really fair? That is what worries me.

I was just a spectator which put me in the position of a judge. Which I hated, because it was a difficult question. They were both Mensa Members and they looked to me as President in the inevitable quarrel.

Marvin was the best golfer but Sandy knew his weakness. He was easily put off. It was at the Sixth hole where the tee is near the road. We are used to the traffic but what Sandy did was this. As Marvin was about to drive a funeral cortege began slowly to pass. Sandy took his hat off with great ceremony and stood rigidly to attention. Poor Marvin had to do the same. The slow procession took ages to pass. When he drove, Marvin went straight into what we call the Five Stroke Bunker.

197

Marvin went white, then red. Then he said slowly and deliberately. 'That was the filthiest bit of gamesmanship I have ever experienced and I believe it was deliberate. I do not wish to play with you any more.'

I admit that Sandy was apologetic. 'I know it was awful for you Marvin,' he said, 'And I admit I was out of order. I'll give you the hole. But try to see my side. What could I do. After all she was my wife, I was married to her for fifteen years.' A very difficult case for a President to judge!

Now here is an even more difficult Kickself Motion Puzzle for you to judge.

A gramophone record is 12 in diameter, it has a 4 in black centre and a 1 in outer border. If the groove is 90 to the inch, how far does the needle travel?

See Answer No A46

P56 Space Race Base

The sky-saucer landed near Woolwich but the little purple Space Race creature must have come down by other means because I found him in my garden at Blackheath dying of thirst three days later. The poor little creature was behind a begonia. It knew our language because I could distinctly hear its expiring whimper. 'Nitric acid! Nitric acid! For Gods Sake! Nitric Acid!' It had been asking a lawn mower to take it to its leader.

There was much to be learned. When we got some acid and made it comfortable we got confused over numbers. But it was ill, and only two of its statements were true. Nevertheless you are expected to work out what the number base of the Space Race is.

1) It told me that 18 and 41 are prime numbers.
2) It said that $7 \times 8 = 62$.
3) 35 is a prime.
4) 63 is evenly divisible by 4.

Which of the four statements were true and what was the Space Race Base?

See Answer No A56

P57 The Case of the Weeping Policeman

When I got to be a cheeky cockney lad of thirteen in Plumstead I used to take on my tiny, witty, spherical Cockney Mum in spite of her marvellous aim with crockery.

I would come in licking my toffee apple, with a worried face and say.

'I'm upset! Imagine it Mum! A great big policeman. Broke down in tears.'

'Who? What happened?'

'You know the one, the fat one that stands opposite the Third Arsenal Gates. All the kids standing round and him crying his eyes out.'

'Why?' I got ready to dodge.

'Well! I wouldn't give him a lick of this toffee apple.'

Here is a real problem to make a policeman weep.

A pensioner buys a radio for eleven pounds but gets hard up and sells it for fifteen pounds to a stranger. He takes a cheque for 25 pounds giving the shifty little buyer 10 pounds change. A neighbour cashed the cheque which bounced, so the poor pensioner had to borrow 25 pounds to pay the neighbour back.

The police problem is to make out how much the thief stole, how much did the poor pensioner lose. And now it's your problem. Over to you.

See Answer No A66

P58 The Biggest Niff

Some Unwhite tribesman had mistakenly captured an Insanitary White Tramp and were betting about which had the worst Niff, the Tramp or a Particularly Niffy Goat. There was a lot of money in the pot when the Trial was arranged. They brought in the Goat and several of them fainted. But when they brought in the malodorous Tramp the Goat fainted.

Having got to a goat I can now set the problem.

A goat was tethered to a post by a rope which was 21 feet

long, the goat therefore grazed over an area of a circle of 21 feet radius.

The owner of the field built a shed 14 feet by 7 feet using the post as a corner post of the shed.

This reduced the grazing area. If the rent was £100 per annum, by how much should the rent be reduced proportionate to the grazing area lost?

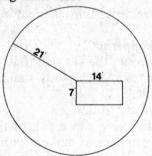

See Answer No A76

P59 How Many Chess Sets?

I learned the moves from a friend, joined the Chess Club and got the Club Captain in the first knockout draw. I beat him. He was looking for subtleties in what was simply Idiotic Play.

Why anyone should ask I do not know. But I do ask. Here is a single chess set and board. The pieces are distinct (every piece has an identity number). How many ways are there correctly to set up the board to begin a game of normal chess. Could you go through them?

See Answer No A86

P60 All Only Now Quickly

'You will eat all your Nice Dinner. You will eat only your Nice Dinner. You will eat your Nice Dinner Now. You will eat Your Nice Dinner Quickly,' said my Mother.

'Certainly Mum. I will Mum. But can I leave the Nasty Fat and have some toffees. And can I start when I finish this Chapter of Amazing Stories. It aint 'arf good.'

I ate it all. I ate nothing else. I ate it immediately and quickly. I was trained in a hard school and have no mercy in me.

In this miserable skeleton of a Crossword you will use All the Alphabet. You will use Only the Alphabet. You will use Each Letter Once Only. You will find an English Dictionary word for each array. You will work quickly.

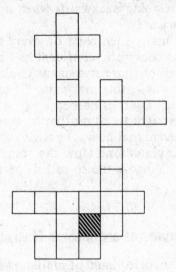

See Answer No A96

P61 Can a Train Go Two Ways At Once?

If you can recognise rubbish when you hear it you are better than most of us.

My Father used to test my capacity for healthy scepticism by making a mixture of truthful and untruthful, unlikely assertions.

If, for instance, he said the sun rotated round the earth he would give every sort of argument for the proposition to see how I countered it. Then he would swear that the moon rotates round the sun and I would deny that too. Your question is was I right?

Sometimes the propositions were so absurdly false that it was no problem to stick to one's guns.

For instance he said

1) There is a solid, physical part of a travelling railway train which is moving in the opposite direction to the rest of the train. It is a part of the train, not of its contents.

2) The part is firmly attached to the train and remains with it all the time.

3) The part is going backwards when all the rest of the train is going forwards.

4) There are many such parts on every travelling train.

For once I was cocky and confident as I pointed out that there is no way all of those statements could be true and he had to admit he was testing me again. Of course! That was my test overcome. Yours is harder.

Was my father right to admit that he was wrong?

In the absurd event that he was wrong to admit it, what can possibly be the explanation? How can some parts be 'going the wrong way?' What is the so called 'part?'

See Answer No A7

P62 Musical Instruments and Musical Machines

Here is an oddly assorted band of mutilated instruments. See if you can fill the missing letters in.

```
_  A  _  O  _
_  I  _  A  _
_  I  _  H  _  R
_  I  _  E
_  A  _  A  _  A  _  K  _
_  O  _  T  _  O  _  N
_  H  _  W  _
_  A  _  T  _  M
_  E  _  E  _  T  _
_  A  _  K  _  U  _
```

See Answer No A17

P63 I Give You Letters You Give Me Words

Let me be frank. The words you are looking for here are esoteric and difficult. But with *ALL* the letters given *AND* in the right order *AND* a simple clue it will be black disgrace if you do not get them.

And that is not all. I have noted with stern if mild approval that you are one of the readers who have survived in this book to well past half-way. Indulgent to the point of mawkishness I now give you a further advantage. I have ringed the letters of the first word so you shall have an example. There now! What more can I do?

Clues

1 Type of fern
2 Meagre
3 First day of August
4 Heavy stone
5 Rough silk fabric
6 Day's labour
7 African tree
8 Itinerant tinker
9 Small bone
10 Itinerant quack
11 Heavy dark sherry
12 Get away with you (slang)

K	J	C	D	L	B	I	D	O
M	A	O	O	I	O	E	G	O
L	L	J	U	A	S	S	E	O
R	D	T	R	C	B	I	O	U
N	M	L	M	R	U	A	V	S
I	P	E	C	I	O	M	B	T
E	O	S	U	N	I	E	B	C
L	A	O	C	O	A	N	H	N
A	I	D	N	K	E	K	S	E

See Answer No A27

P64 Ingeniously Difficult

Problem setters are the most perverse, preposterous, barse ackwards people who ever sucked air. Humanity uses all its craft, intelligence, skill and ingeniousness to solve the billions of problems that the Universe presents to Mind, that infinitesmally small sample of itself.

Problem setters are the Great Exception. They use all those arts and ingenuity to make simple problems more complex and to create problems where there were none.

You will hate this further Examples of Misplaced Ingenuity. Crosswords can be as difficult and tough as any one would require. But I invented Wigglewords because crosswords seemed to be too effete, straightforward, and comprehensible.

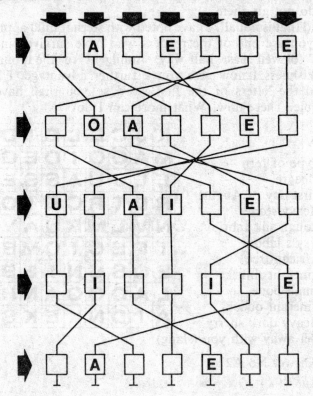

See Answer No. A37

P65 I Give Crossword. You Work Out Pattern

This is Ken Russell's perverse and confusing idea. Overwhelmingly the crossword composer gives you the pattern and you fill in the words from the clues. Ken knows a trick worth two of that. He starts you off with the filled in Crossword but fills the black squares with a lot of random rubbish, or worse, deliberately deceptive false clues.

Your job is to find out and fill in the black squares of the pattern so that a full, consistent crossword results. The pattern is a normal symmetrical balanced one. Another Blatant Example Of Misplaced Ingenuity.

I	N	D	I	V	I	D	U	A	L	I	S	T
N	U	R	S	E	R	E	S	I	G	N	O	H
F	L	E	U	R	E	T	E	R	E	V	U	E
I	V	A	N	G	R	E	A	S	E	A	R	R
N	U	R	S	E	D	R	H	A	B	D	O	M
E	C	E	E	V	O	I	E	I	E	E	M	O
T	H	R	E	E	C	O	R	N	E	R	E	D
E	V	E	A	F	A	R	I	T	R	U	L	Y
S	A	G	I	T	T	A	P	S	A	P	A	N
I	N	R	O	A	D	T	E	W	N	H	N	A
M	O	O	S	E	N	I	R	I	D	I	U	M
A	D	U	R	G	E	V	I	S	T	A	X	I
L	E	P	T	O	C	E	P	H	A	L	I	C

See Answer No A47

P66 Look At It Which Way You Like

'Look at it which way you like, it all comes to the same thing.' How many times have you have that said to you? Nearly always it is wrong. It is only rarely that the point of view makes no difference.

Now in a Russell Square it really does not matter which way you look at it. Down or across it reads the same.

Three legged stand
Drink liquor habitually
Unfold
Buy back
Makes hats
Come to destination

See Answer No A57

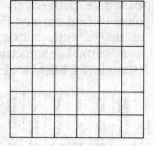

P67 Feydau Farce Puzzle

I love doors. They are essential to civilisation. Without them we are animals, with them we are gods. They ensure privacy, property, love, friendship and they are great fun. In French farces like those by Feydau, a gang of fast moving characters are forever popping in and out of many doors. Take away his doors and Feydau would have written nothing but dreary Dostoyevskian tragedies. A stage set without doors is like a tongueless orator or an armless mime. A room without a door is like a woman without eyelids, a stopperless bottle of lager, or a lidless dustbin.

Let there be more doors. How could you be snug and cosy indoors, on a winter evening, without a good set of solid doors?

So that is why Ken Russell's curious triangular, many doored house is so fascinating. You may compose your own Feydau farce and spell the encrypted 15 letter word at the same time as you rush around the odd building, of which the plan is given. Find where to start, then go round opening and banging doors, dodging in and out of the corridors as much as you like until you have picked up the letters in the right order. One visit to each room should suffice. Miss no room. What is the word that is hidden behind the doors?

206

See Answer No A67

P68 Chancing It With Octahedral Dice

A pair of eight faced dice would be hard to get hold of but if you did what would they look like and what would be the odds against throwing a six with a pair of them.

See Answer No A77

P69 Do You Love Jesus?

A little man with the dark untidy hair and a tense manner sits opposite a large placid Dutch tourist in the Edinburgh train. The Dutchman reads his paper while the young man fidgets and looks uneasy. There is a fanatical gleam in his eyes.

The young man speaks. He has a problem. He is concerned about the Dutchman's soul.

He leans forward earnestly.

'Do you love Jesus?'

The Dutchman asks his pardon.

'Do you really, really, love Jesus?'

'Ah! Jesus, I must to be frank by you. Here I do not love Jesus at all. By England I do not love Jesus. For me is horrible the English Jesus. But I am very liking the little round Dutch Jesus which I am having by Rotterdam.'

Which with my accustomed obliquity brings me to the subject of the puzzle. Cheeses.

There is a beautiful world of cheeses and I want to see if you know it as every sybarite should.

Every second letter is lost in the names of these well known and less well known cheeses. Find the missing letters and complete the tasty cheeses.

1) __ A __ E __ B __ R __   7) __ R __ Y __ R __

2) __ O __ G __ N __ O __ A   8) __ E __ L __ C __ O __

3) __ M __ E __ T __ A __   9) __ H __ S __ I __ E

4) __ O __ U __ F __ R __   10) __ A __ M __ S __ N

5) __ E __ V __ A __   11) __ I __ B __ R __ E __

6) __ I __ S __ T __ R   12) __ O __ D __

See Answer No A87

P70 A Bit Out

The Klondyke gold miner Lem was in trouble. There had been a survey mixup. The next claim, that of Tom, covered part of his own as shown in the diagram so that according to the records both had a claim to the same section (shaded). The corner of Tom's much larger rectangular claim was on the centre of his and the intersection was, as shown, just 102 feet from one corner of Lem's 305 foot square claim. Tom's claim was 387 × 406 feet.

Lem had struck it rich and decided that the only way to

208

keep out of delay and litigation was to share the yield of the mine. Receipts would be reckoned according to area and Tom should have half of what was allocated to the area in dispute. But neither knew geometry. Nor did any one else within 300 miles.

Lem was bright and found a way to work out the fair proportion without calculation or ground measurement. He demonstrated on a drawing. It convinced Tom because it was obvious. How did they decide what proportion of Lem's claim was in dispute? What was the proportion?

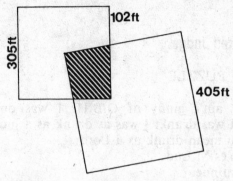

See Answer No A97

P71 Stretching Things

One of the assumptions a jogger makes is that each mile is the same length. It seemed a reasonably safe assumption until Einstein insisted that the length of a mile relative to the standing observer depends upon the speed of the traveller. A rough model of this follows: The traveller is on a piece of stretched elastic marked in megametres. The faster he moves the more the elastic is relaxed and the slower his clock goes from the observer's viewpoint not his own. The traveller counts the inaccurate marks, gazes at his faulty watch and running his heart out, is unaware of the rotten trick.

It all sounds as if those two fools are guinea pigs in some cosmic experiment. They ought to get together and check up.

Which is why I feel for the poor bewildered ant in this

unpleasant experiment.

A three inch long elastic band is fixed at one end. An ant crawls along it at one inch per minute. After one minute the band is stretched three inches. The ant then crawls along at the same rate and after one minute the band is stretched a further three inches. This cycle continues at the end of each minute until the ant reaches the end of the band. Assuming the band is capable of being stretched so far, how long will it take the ant to reach the end?

See Answer No A8

P72 Frustrated Judge

KICKSELF PUZZLE

Prisoner I ain't guilty of G.B.H. I was only arrested because I was drunk. I was as drunk as a judge.
Judge You mean drunk as a Lord.
Prisoner Yes M'Lud.
Judge Continue.
Pristoner As God is my Judge, Your Honour, I am not guilty.
Judge He is not. I am. You are. Three months. With costs.

But things were difficult for the Judge in his next case.

In accordance with the wishes of the majority and despite the objections of the enlightened, Capital Punishment had been restored in the land.

When the prisoner was found guilty, the Judge pronounced the Sentence.

'Yours,' he said to the man in the dock 'was an especially heinous crime and one which was all the worse because you obviously anticipated my dilemma at this moment. According to the new law I have no alternative but to sentence you to immediate execution. But, as you have been brazen enough to boast, I can pass such a sentence but it cannot be carried out.'

The man was in custody, guilty, young, healthy, sane, single and had no power to harm the judge or anyone else.

210

How was it that the judge was powerless to do justice as the law required?

See Answer No A18

P73 Tile Overseers

Since it has been established to the satisfaction of some left-wards persons that Property is Theft, the guarding of property is a form of aggression and the prosecution of those who 'steal' property, an injustice. However if the takers-away or 'thieves' have now acquired the property . . . property is theft so . . . Let me start again, I am getting muddled.

Some unjust, exploiting, property owners had acquired a house and had covered the floor with tiles which were admittedly their own property. They did not want to ask any-one to do the disgraceful work of guardian so they allocated the role to conscienceless robots.

In the diagram you will see how they were stationed. The robots   can detect 'intruders' in the across, down and diagonal lines of tiles that they are in. So the small 16 tile square is fully guarded but some tiles are not.

Your question is this. What is the most oppressive arrange-ment of these evil robots, i.e. what is the largest area of tiles that can be 'guarded' with the team of five?

Move the robots to the positions where the largest area of tiles is 'protected' against those who wish to Liberate the property in the Name of All the People.

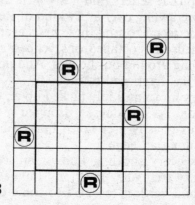

See Answer No A28

P74 Whatever Have They Got In Common?

The most disparate couples marry and prompt the title question. Often what is in common is not easily seen. You get this sort of thing. 'Well, Algernon is a dermatologist you see, and we were drawn together by my acne.'

'What have we two got in common,' I asked once of a girl with whom I was flirting.

'I can tell you that,' she said, 'We are both madly in love with you.' There was more wit than truth in her.

So I come to the point.

Here is a list of words. All except one belong to the same class, have some very distinctive property in common.

TRAMPS, BRANDY, SCAMPI, PLAIT, STORES, PIRATED

Which is the stranger in the camp? What is the property common to the rest.

There are longer words which have the same property. Can you find any more?

See Answer No A38

P75 My Icosahedron's Infestation

For some reason beyond even my wide ranging, penetrating sapience, puzzle setters find nasty little disease ridden insects constantly crawling over every kind of Regular Solid Object. No-one else seems to find these pests every time they pick up the tetrahedrons, octahedrons, cubes and paralellopipeds that are lying around our houses. And now that I am setting puzzles it has happened to me!

This very morning I idly picked up an ordinary household icosahedron. As one does. I dropped it with horror when I noticed this ghastly grey-green horned bug with puce spots crawling along an edge.

Now as every suckling knows, an icosahedron has just these twenty triangular faces and the necessary complement of edges and vertices (corners to some of you).

Like this.

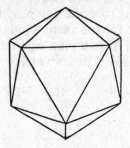

I watched the beastly unwinged, little insect. It was crawling along the edges very slowly and I knew what it was trying to do. It clearly wanted to leave its sticky green germ-laden tracks on every edge so as to infect anyone who picked up this much handled and essential household object. It was a crawler not a hopper.

It was obviously vital to work out how long it would take to complete this fell plan. It crawled at one edge per minute so how long would it take fully to infect all edges? How long had I got to call in the Local Icosahedron Insect Pest Control Officer with his Noddy Suit, Mask and Bug Gun.

See Answer No A48

P76 Maritime Variety Reduction

The earnest young man in puzzle 69 continued his conversation with the kindly Dutchman who hated English Cheeses.

The evangelist asked about the Dutchman's soul. The Dutchman looked puzzled. 'Soul? What soul? A soul that is coming from a boot?'

'No I did not mean a leather sole.'

'I did not either mean a leather sole. I mean a sole what swims in sea.'

'But that is not a leather sole, it is a fish. It does not come from a boot.'

Yes of course it does come from a boot, a fishing boot.'

The evangelist decided to let this one soul manage for itself.

There is a lot of confusion about boats.

This puzzle is going to make you pray for maritime variety reduction. There are far too many kinds of boats, about one per three boatmen. I have a plan where there will be a range of International Standard Boats which will come in five sizes. And that will be it.

```
 _  A  _  L
 _  E  _  E  _
 _  C  _  O  _  N  _  R
 _  E  _  U  _  C  _
 _  I  _  D  _  A  _  M  _  R
 _  R  _  I  _  H  _  E  _
 _  U  _  N  _  U  _  R  _  M  _
 _  A  _  L  _  O  _
 _  U  _  B  _  A  _
 _  A  _  A  _  A  _  A  _
 _  O  _  D  _  L  _
 _  I  _  N  _  C  _
```

See Answer No A58

P77 Russell Square Manes

Here are five attached Russell Squares with the diagonal triplets forming the letters of manes.

The manes are those of the three horses which were drawing the chariot of the Lovely Warrior Goddess whose statue used to be in that or some other square.

The five Russell Squares have the same five words down and across. 25 words in all. The 25 clues are in random order.

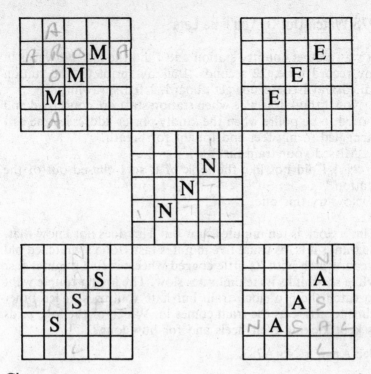

Clues

1 Chatter
2 Small civet
3 Of the nose *NASAL*
4 Progeny *ISSUE*
5 Dramatic performance
6 Lively jazz dance
7 Fragrance *AROMA*
8 Brisk
9 Ray
10 Plait
11 Drinker
12 Scolds
13 Horse

4 Staff of office
15 Worth
16 Greek letter
17 Pulls apart
18 Void
19 Tooth
20 Extent
21 Type of plaster
22 Between *INTER*
23 Cease
24 Books
25 Having wings

See Answer No A68

P78 Watch Out Or You'll Be Late

It was a quiet country station and I did the last 100 yards in my record time, 22 seconds. But my sprint up the station failed and I could not get aboard. I fell sprawling.

Now I think it is nice when station staff are concerned and I tried to be polite when the kindly porter addressed me as I struggled to my feet and fought for breath.

'Missed your train Sir?'

'No! I did not like the look of it so I chased out of the station.'

Now try this one.

Tim's clock is ten minutes slow but Tim does not know that, he thinks it is, as usual five minutes fast. Julie's wretched old steam watch with its little cogged wheels is five minutes fast while she thinks its ten minutes slow. The loving couple want to catch the 6 o'clock train but hate waiting so each other aims to arrive as the train comes in. Which of the love birds is kept kicking their heels and for how long?

See Answer No A78

P79 A Long Word Hidden

The puzzle is the reverse of the word you seek.

You are in the vile country of Rotonolia. Only Mensa members are allowed to leave it. Rotonolians hate that smart aleck lot. Rotonolians test your intelligence in this crude way, not like Mensa, to accept you, but to give you the National Chuck. Find the route through the 15 rooms as before, visiting each only once but using the corridors as you like. Trace out the hidden password or remain in Rotonolia forever. Find the word and you are back at the mercy of smart aleck Mensans. Dilemma!

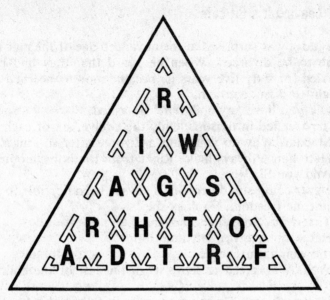

See Answer No A88

P80 Whoppers

After a successful day's fishing George, Henry and Michael stopped at Charley's Bar to quench their thirst and tell Charley about their exploits.

'I caught nine fish,' said George. 'I caught two less than Henry, but one more than Michael.'

'At least I didn't have the smallest catch,' said Henry. The difference between my catch and Michael's was three fish. Michael caught 12.'

'I caught fewer than George,' said Michael. 'George caught 10. Henry caught three more than George.'

Each of the men had just downed six pints of beer, so it is understandable that they all made one wrong statement out of three. How many fish did each catch?

See Answer No A98

P81 Leaving it a Bit Late

The judge was surprised at the advanced age of the pair that came to be divorced. When he heard that they had been married for sixty five years he became more concerned and sought to dissuade them.

'Did you have any children?' he asked.

They replied in unison, 'Only the twelve, six of each.'

'Madam. Why do you want a divorce after so long?'

'Hate him. Always have. Right from the honeymoon.'

'And you Sir.'

'Never could stand her. She's always been horrible to me. I want me freedom. So does she.'

'That I do. Sooner the better.'

'But why have you left it so long?'

The woman answered.

'Well. We agreed to leave it till the last of the children died.'

Your problem? Their birthdays both fell on the 4th July. They were born seven years apart. The man was 2555 days older than his wife.

In which years were they born? It is a Kickself.

See Answer No A9

P82 Birds and Bees

The Smiths and the Jones live next door to each other. Each family has five children, and the five Smith children have the same names as the five Jones children. As was bound to happen, they soon paired off, but no pair shared the same names.

Fran Jones dated the Smith boy who had the same name as the girl who was dating Sidney Smith.

Leslie Smith was taller than the boy she went out with.

Chris Smith dated the boy who had the same name as Pat Jones's boyfriend.

Who was Chris Jones dating?

See Answer No A19

218

P83 Hereward T. Waik

Hereward T. Waik is not a very good sleeper. At 10.15 one night he took a sleeping pill and went to bed. Forty minutes later he had to get up to go to the lavatory and then he went to bed again, counted sheep and fell asleep. Somewhat later, two cats howling outside his window woke him up: he looked at his alarm clock and noticed that the hands were exactly overlapping. He dozed off for a little over a quarter of an hour, woke again and noticed that the hour and minute digits on his clock-radio were all the same. Four and a half hours later he got up for breakfast. What time did he get up?

See Answer No A29

P84 Dicing with Death

The mercenaries attached to an idiosyncratic tribal autocrat captured a rebel force. To subdue and terrify the 64 captured fighters the chief made them dice with death. He had a block of ivory cut into a cube. Then he had the entire surface smeared with the blood of an executed prisoner.

The gory object was then cut up as shown in the drawing. Four cuts through each dimension.

Some of the many little resultings cubes had bloody faces. Some three, some two, some one. But some had none.

The terrified soldiers had to draw a cube from a covered box and throw the small dice while a cheering crowd watched and bet. If the face up was bloody the thrower was put to death.

What was a prisoners chance of dying, the odds in the betting.

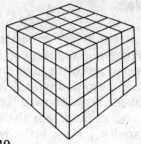

See Answer No A39

P85 An Impossible Anagram

An anagram! Five Ss and Four Es in one word!
'Impossible!' is the natural reaction to this absurd so-called
anagram. Perhaps it is impossible. Perhaps not. Just look at
it! I mean, I ask you!

L L P N S S S S S E E E E

1) Are you wasting your time trying to find a one-word
anagram of this? 2) If not, what is it?

See Answer No A49

P86 Semantic Dualism

The human brain seems to have an inbuilt dualistic tendency.
For every triple, four or five fold think-link we make scores
of dual ones. We have pairing minds which semantically
couple things often and triple and quadruple them more
rarely.

And the pairing of opposites is a strong tendency too. The
mind might be expected to fly from one thought to another
which is semantically close. It often does the opposite and
flies to the antithesis, a thought which is at the other pole.
Human beings have inbuilt perversity, preposterousness. We
are semantically dipole.

So let us now confuse you with a bi-dualistic problem. The

problem of competitive or paradoxical semantic pairings. That should contain you for a bit. Each word in list A has two possible pairings in list B.

Each word in list B has two possible pairings in list A.

Pair a word in list A with a word in list B until you have 10 pairs.

List A	List B
Penny	Water
Fence	Coin
Ring	Sugar
Moidore	Pale
Doughnut	Epee
White	Torus
Sword	Gold
Beet	Black
Sea	Root
Tap	Fish

There are two answers.

See Answer No A59

P87 Another Dreadful Multidimensional Mixup

With two dimensional crosswords you are probably able to cope. This 3D Acrossdownthroughword is designed to overstretch you. We give you the threespace frame. We even give you the answer, all the words. Your task is simply to fit them in to the frame. There are five Russell Squares.

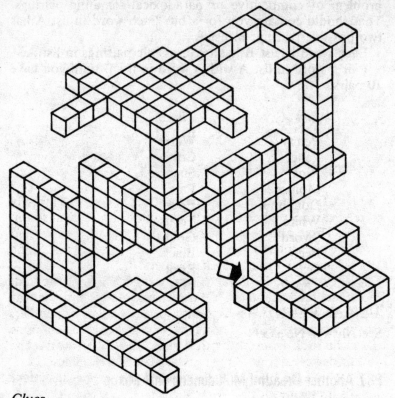

Clues

OPERATIONAL	DANTE	SERFS
SANDBLASTED	DANTE	TRYST
DETERMINE	OPPOSED	TRYST
TRACTION	SCREE	LIGHT
DISAGREE	HOARD	METER
SUPPOSED	EATS	RAIDS
STRUMPET	ATE	RAIDS
DETERRENT	RED	IRATE
DRUBBED	RATED	AGREE
TWISTERS	BLAST	IRATE
LOWERED	AWARE	SEERS
WAVERED	SERVED	SEERS
SHEARED	LOWER	RAVEL
TWISTERS	AWARE	UVULA

ERECTED	SERVE	MELON
COATED	TREES	TRUMP
SEVEN	TREES	RAVEL
SEVEN	IVORY	UVULA
POSED	SERFS	MELON
ERECT	WAVER	PLANK
OPERA	IVORY	PLANK

See Answer No A69

P88 Kickself: Mr Nasty Parker

The Traffic Warden passed along a street and saw 12 illegally parked cars. So he left a summons under all 12 windscreen wipers. Three hours later he returned. Three of the cars had gone but their places had been occupied by other cars. So he left a summons under all three wipers.

Now one of the 15 illegal parkers was Mr Nasty Parker. All the others paid up but he did not. He owned the parked car and there was nothing wrong with its registration or number. But he was untraceable despite the properly written summons which he took from under this wiper and threw away. The authorities even found out his trick but were helpless.

What was the Evil Trick by which he avoided punishment for his mesdemeanour.

See Answer No A79

P89 Followwordirectionotypical

This is another one of Ken Russell's unpleasant puzzles in which he spells words any which way. He starts at 1, spells towards 2 wherever it is in the grid, then on 3 and so on. As if that were not confusing enough he is using the last letter of one word to begin the next word as the title here illustrates. That is how we would all spell if he had his way. Very poor show! I'm not surprised that you will never solve it.

Clues

1 Flowers (9)
2 Scamp (9)
3 Assembly (9)
4 Mathematician (8)
5 Bearing (8)
6 Chinese puzzle (7)
7 Wonders (7)
8 Shoe (5)
9 Flask (7)
10 Distrust (7)
11 Female tiger (7)
12 Slide (4)
13 Cuts (5)
14 Drink slowly (3)   16 Slender (4)
15 Shut in (4)   17 Cob (3)

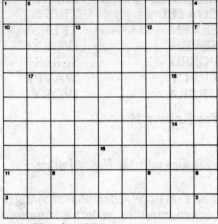

See Answer No A89

P90 Name Punched in Metal

In my young days, life was full of wonder, especially the seaside. The slot machines fascinated the small cheeky coppernob that I was. I could have hours of amusement with a pocket of pennies.

The one wonder of modern technology was a shiny brass machine with a big dial which you could rotate. The letters of the alphabet were arranged around it and by rotating and pulling a lever you could punch the letters of your *OWN NAME* on to an aluminium strip. You could even keep the strip when it fell out of the machine.

I have this interesting strip by me yet. 'VICTIR SEREBRIAKO' it says. The machine rationed letters and I made only one mistake! Think of it. For a penny! And an old penny, at that. Most of my name!

Now one day the machine was out of kilter and was printing the next letter to the one indicated as the diagram shows on the inside ring.

Your problem is to find one or more four letter (or if you

are mad, five letter) words where by spelling on the outer ring one word you get another actual word embossed on the strip. Find a few hundred of such pairs. Or one. If you can!

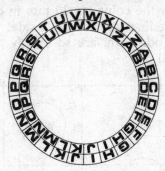

See Answer No A99

P91 More Ghastly Verbectomy

Verbectomy is word surgery. The deliberate degutting of a harmless useful English word so as to make it difficult to recognise.

TSQ	ATTH
CKWH	OCHM
NUPP	TCHH
JORG	SHYW
IFFD	LGAT

See Answer No A10

P92 The Odds on a Rolling Penny

You must have seen the game at fairgrounds. You roll a penny down a little chute and if it lands fully within a square your fortune is made. The fairground man keeps your penny and give you the number of pennies written on the square, as many as five pennies! If the coin lies over a line the triumphant stall keeper sweeps it away and there goes another bag of liquorice allsorts.

But what are the odds. In such vital matters we have to know. Let us say the coins are 20 mm in diameter and the squares inside the lines are 35 mm a side.

What are the odds you are so calmly accepting as you lightheartedly roll.

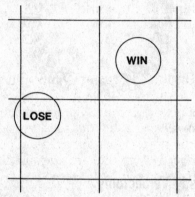

See Answer No A20

P93 Roll Dem Bones Probability Theory

I am fascinated by the fact that all the traditional gamblers' games are based on a correct assessment of the odds in spite of the fact that no one knew how to calculate them. The art of statistics and probability theory was born when gambling French Noblemen enlisted mathematicians. Not the other way round.

But the uninstructed forerunners had it about right already and I guess there must have been an evolutionary process by which good guessers about odds remained in the business. Bad guessers disappeared.

An instance of gamblers getting it about right is the De Mere's Problem. See if you can work it all out instead of taking your chance like a man.

226

De Mere's Problem

Several hundred years ago, gaming houses would offer odds of even money that the gambler would throw at least one six in four throws of a single die. What are the true odds? Also, they bet even money that the gambler would throw a pair of sixes at least once in 24 throws of two dice. Do these odds favour the gambler or the house?

See Answer No A30

P94 They Are Unlettered Squares Throw Them Out!

Hep, turned-on people like me object to the illiterate squares who infest this grid. What should have been the shaded unlettered squares in this crossword have been occupied by outsider, non-member letters, who are masquerading as genuine parts of the crossword so as to deceive and confuse. They should go just as they did in puzzle P65.

I	M	P	E	R	I	O	U	S	N	E	S	S
N	E	I	C	E	T	C	H	E	O	B	E	T
S	C	E	N	A	T	C	L	T	R	O	N	A
E	H	R	E	T	O	I	L	S	U	N	I	T
N	U	T	S	A	N	D	R	O	G	Y	N	E
S	T	I	L	T	E	E	H	V	B	K	O	S
A	C	C	I	D	E	N	T	A	L	I	S	M
T	O	H	G	O	M	T	I	L	E	M	E	A
E	N	C	O	M	I	A	S	T	Y	P	E	N
N	O	R	I	S	Y	L	P	I	E	E	J	L
E	L	E	C	T	A	I	Q	D	E	L	H	I
S	E	E	P	A	G	S	E	E	G	O	U	K
S	U	P	E	R	S	E	N	S	I	B	L	E

See Answer No A40

227

P95 The Devil's Picture Cards

All puzzles are, to some extent tests of intelligence. This one tests your knowledge but also something which is much more important. Your decency and Godliness. There are those who work as priests, police or judges whose duty forces them to soil their knowledge with such things as card games and all the other Devil's devices to divert and betray.

The test here is how badly you do. There is very little chance of Eternal Life for those who do well at this puzzle unless they are the honourable gentlemen of the professions I have named.

Test yourself without flinching. If you are to have an Eternity of Torment it is as well to be prepared.

CARD GAMES

Alternate letters are missing, see if you can fill them in. Not as easy as it may appear!

```
__ U __ H __ E
__ C __ R __ E
__ A __ T __ N
__ I __ Q __ E __
__ R __ B __ A __ E
__ U __ D __ I __ L __
__ E __ I __ U __
__ I __ O __ L __
__ U __ M __
__ A __ A __ T __
__ O __ I __ A __ R __
__ A __ C __ R __ T
```

See Answer No A50

P96 A Mensa Special Interest Group

Mensa has no policy and no objectives, collectively. It aims to collect intelligent people from all sides of society and of all views. But individual members have strong views and those who share a view or interest form Special Interest Groups or *SIGS* as we call them.

We have all sorts of *SIGS*. Chess *SIGS*, Philosophy *SIGS*, Business *SIGS*, Maths *SIGS*, Apathy *SIGS*, Politics *SIGS* and what have you.

This concerns the very popular Temperance *SIG* which sometimes has Joint Meetings with the Boozer's *SIG* and The Delirium Tremens *SIG*.

Five members of the Temperance *SIG* were sitting at the bar, trying out of pure philanthropy to diminish the World's sins by disposing of its stocks of liquor. Alexander was sitting closer to Beth than Clarence was to Alexander. Dorothy was seated between Beth and Alexander, but not necessarily next to either one of them. Clarence was seated on Ernest's right, but Beth was not seated next to Ernest. From left to right, in what order were they sitting?

See Answer No A60

P97 Which Is Wrong?

My Chairman used to be adept at finding the one, often unimportant, doubtful figure in a lengthy presentation. One glance at a page of figures and his stubby finger was stabbed at the error.

Let us see how you do.

Here are 12 groups of four figures. You do not know what these figures are about. You have the advantage of knowing that one line of four figures is wrong. There are an infinite number of possible answers. You are looking for the likely one. You could find a rationale for making any line the odd one out but there is one which is much less contrived than the others. Where is the error? Which line contains faults? What is there in common between all the other sets?

1)	187	58	13	135
2)	136	10	61	180
3)	170	142	97	270
4)	357	106	53	270
5)	119	4	19	45
6)	340	58	23	45
7)	289	160	3	135
8)	323	90	17	450
9)	237	184	22	120
10)	289	128	43	270
11)	289	36	73	135
12)	136	60	11	225

See Answer No A70

P98 A Family Party

In my cockney youth a party with relations could be a night of uproarious jollity with hours of music and a prolonged 'knees up' dance until people dropped in laughing exhaustion. Equally, it could finish up as a running street fight. Chancy, is what family parties used to be then.

My company, Family Party Insurance Ltd., works to the principle that the less people at a family party the better the chances of avoiding claims. So we must know the number to be present. Here is a proposal. At Mary's party there will be: Her Mother, her Mother's sister-in-law. her sister, her sister's Mother-in-law, her Mother-in-law's sister, her sister-in-law's Mother, and her next door neighbour.

As Insurer Against Party Mayhem I know that, given the proposal above, there is the smallest possible party. We know relations are legal and not incestuous. In order to quote a premium I need to know the number present. How many will there be? How are they related.

See Answer No A80

230

P99 The Aged Mensan Tycoon

The aged Mensan tycoon wanted to leave his great wealth to the most intelligent of his children and, being the victim of senile silliness, devised an undignified game for them to play to test their wits. The lawyers were told to fill in a blank will in favour of the first of the seven children to bring them the location of the golden key. The key was hidden beneath one of the large tiles in the old man's study. The key was not under either of the two desks marked.

The room was locked and the contestants had the map you see.

These were the conditions the decrepit old man devised.

Start where the N is marked.

Enter the words given in the list.

The words must be entered to read in any direction N, S, E or W according to the first letter in them, which is also the last letter of the previous word. The Golden Key is under the last letter placed. The words are listed.

The key was found by a quiet little girl of 10 and the whole family spent the next 20 years in lawsuits. But which tile hid the golden key?

NODULE
NATURE
NETTLE
NEE
NOTICE

EDITS WIDENS
ELAN   WILTON
EDGES WANTON
EEL
ELFIN
E

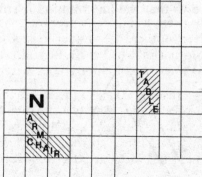

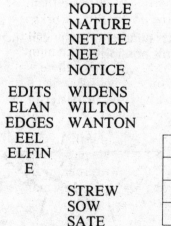

STREW
SOW
SATE
SPATS

SHADOW

See Answer No A90

P100 Turn Line. Keep in Touch

Congratulations! You have come to the last hurdle or at least sneak-peeked at it. Do not fall at this fence. It is going to be a tough one. A real tester with which to finish.

Here is an equilateral triangle with a line in it and it is obvious that if we rotate the line laterally without changing its length, it cannot stay with both ends touching the sides of the triangle.

1) So can this be done?

Without changing the position of the three vertices of the triangle, draw, within it, a shape including the vertices which enables you to rotate the line in the plane of the paper while keeping it in constant contact with your figure at both of its ends.

   Can it be done and what shape is it if it can?

2) Can a five point star be modified in the same way so that the line can be rotated inside it while keeping its ends in contact with the star and touching every point in the perimeter?

3) If that can be done what other number of cusps can there be so that the line rotation is still possible?

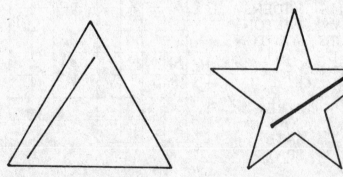

See Answer No A100

The Answers

Answer No A1 P1 Abracadabra

You got in a muddle did you not. You tried to count them and lost track. Wrong! You should have *calculated* the answer. There are two ways from A to B. For each of those two ways there are two ways to the R rank. For each of these four routes there are two ways to the next A rank and so on. Since there are ten ranks below the A, we multiply by two, 10 times to get the answer, $2^{10} = 1024$ ways to spell ABRACADABRA or gibberish. A sensible use of your time? Huh!

Answer No A2 P11 Every Man His Own King

SYNONYMS FOR SEAT

1 THRONE   2 BENCH   3 RUMBLE
4 ARMCHAIR   5 TRICLINIUM   6 SETTEE
7 DIVAN   8 OTTOMAN   9 POUFFE
10 HOWDAH 11 DICKEY   12 FAUTEUIL

Answer No A3 P21 A Bit Out of the Middle

ORPHAN HOOD   SMOCK-FROCK
CONGRESS-WOMAN   BURNING-GLASS
GESELLSCHAFT   MASTIGOPHORA
BRACHYDACTYL   SILICICOLOUS
CONTRA-FAGOTTO   MEZZO-RELIEVO

Answer No A4 P31 Recognising Forms of Nothing

Answer No A5   P41   Kickself: Personholes
Round personholes are safer than other shapes because the round cover cannot fall down the hole. The square or rectangular or even the eliptical one can.

Answer No A6   P51   Snap!
As is usual with problems of this type it is easier to find the chances that an event will not happen.

The chances that there will *not* be a 'snap' are

$$\left(\frac{51}{52}\right)^{52} = 0.3643$$

ie: "no snap" 36.43% chance.
   "snap" = 63.57% chance.

Answer No A7   P61   Can a Train Go Two Ways at Once
I was wrong to deny the moon rotates round the Sun. My father's other four statements were not false, they are simultaneously true and he was wrong to admit error.

The many parts of the train that are going the wrong way are the tips of the flanges of each of the wheels. The tangent point on a wheel must be stationary relative to the rail but the flange below the rail moves backwards.

Answer No A8   P71   Stretching Things
10.781355 minutes. When the elastic is stretched the ant moves with it and here are the lengths at each stage.

ELASTIC	ANT REACHED
distance 6″	2″
distance 9″	4.5″
distance 12″	7.333333″
distance 15″	10.41667″
distance 18″	13.7″
distance 21″	17.15″
distance 24″	20.74286″
distance 27″	24.46071″
distance 30″	28.28968″
distance 33″	32.21865″

time = 10.78135 minutes

Such elastic! From three to 33 inches is stretching things a bit. As

234

for the ant, the poor bewildered thing, its goal was receding even though it was gaining ground it did not know about.

Answer No A9   P81   Leaving it a Bit Late
1896 and 1903. The clue is that the days are an exact multiple of 365 so there was no Leap Year in between. That means the date had to straddle a century end when there is no leap year. The only recent dates that satisfy the birthdays are those given.

Answer No A10   P91   More Ghastly Verbectomy
Setsquare   Kilowatt-hour   Buckwheat   Epoch-making
Swan-upping   Wytch-hazel   Major-general
Wishy-washy   Sheriffdom   Woolgathering

Answer No A11   P2   Every Which Way

C	S	U	I	R	A	N	E	D
H	R	C	T	E	U	D	E	D
O	P	I	I	I	E	C	E	N
U	O	M	N	S	N	N	O	U
N	V	H	U	O	S	G	G	O
D	A	S	C	I	L	I	E	P
E	I	S	T	E	R	I	L	X
D	N	Y	A	C	H	T	N	E
E	T	T	E	L	U	A	P	E

Answer No A12   P12   Kickself Problem Class Consciousness
12 Part 1 Kickself Answer is, the letter Z.

The capital letters 'S H O N I X Z' are the only ones which are the same upside down. Reverse them and they are unchanged. All the others do not survive reversal.

Answer No A13   P22   Hard Words
1   JOCUND   2   OCTROI   3   PARAQUAT
4   RAMAL   5   SCANSORIAL   6   TALAPOIN
7   TETRAD   8   VALGUS   9   TISANE
10   XIPHOID   11   YTTRIUM   12   ZEPHYR

Answer No A14   P32   Problem for an Impatient Lazy Man
12,344 matches. There is only one winner so there must be 12,344 losers. In a knock-out two-handed game like chess there has to be one game for each contestant eliminated. 12,344 miserable losers, 12,344 games. Viola!

Answer No A15   P42   The Message
Shy gypsy, slyly, spryly, tryst, by my crypt.

Answer No A16   P52   Two of a Kind
Having selected one card, black or red, 4 of the remaining cards will pair, 5 will not. Chances are therefore, Will 4 out of 9. Will not 5 out of 9.

Answer No A17   P62   MUSICAL INSTRUMENTS AND MUSICAL MACHINES
TABOR   SITAR   ZITHER   PIPE OR
FIFE   BALALAIKA   POSTHORN
SHAWM   TAMTAM   CELESTE   SACKBUT

Answer No A18   P72   Frustrated Judge. Idle Executionier
The man was one of a pair of undetachable Siamese twins. He had killed his brother's wife in a jealous rage after knocking his twin brother unconscious. To execute the murderer would also be to kill the victim's innocent husband. The villain could not even be imprisoned without grave injustice to the wronged one. Solomon! Advice please?

Answer No A19   P82   Birds and Bees
Leslie Smith.

Answer No A20   P92   The Odds on a Rolling Penny

For you to win the centre of the coin must fall within the 15mm square within the large square. For you there is a 15×15 mm square. Against you there is the rest of a 35×35 mm square. An hour or two with a calculator should bring you to the result. The odds are 4.4444 (4.4 recurring) to 1.

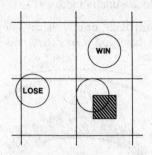

Answer No A21   P3   Trilogical Acrossdownthroughword

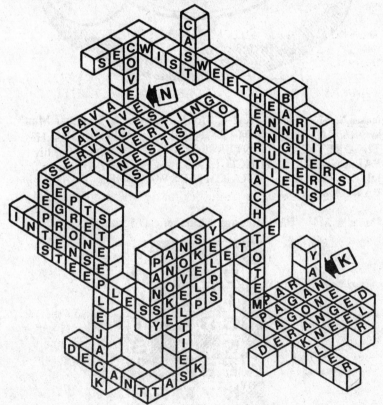

Answer No A22   P13   The Yonklowvitz Diamond
A   The unequivocal answer is yes. You could turn it inside out.

B The shape would be unchanged.

C This is a very difficult one. I lied. They will NOT still be interlinked. Against common sense they will become unlinked as shown in the diagram.

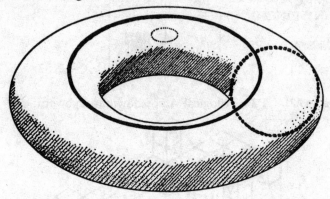

Answer No A23   P23   Hey! C'Mon! Let's Get It Together Man!
WORKMANSHIP   MARTINGALE   WITHERING
THEORETICAL   INTERSECTION   CONSONANT
PARALLAX   CHINCHILLAS   CANDIDATE
DISCOURAGE   STRAIGHTFORWARDNESS
PANTOMINE

Answer No A24   P33   Blatant Alphabetic Discrimination

Answer No A25   P43   Operation Hara Kiri
SNOW-GOGGLES   SNAGGLE-TOOTHED
SKIMBLE-SKAMBLE   HOBBLEDEHOY
BETWEENNESS   LAKE-DWELLING
STOMACH-PUMP   GET-TOGETHER
PENNY-PINCHING   TRANS-SHIPMENT

Answer No A26   P53   Pulling Stars to Pieces

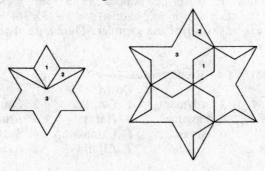

Answer No A27   P63   I Give You Letters You Give Me Words
1 OSMUND   2 JEJUNE   3 LAMMAS
4 KILLICK   5 DUPION   6 CORVEE
7 BAOBAB   8 DIDICOI   9 OSSICLE
10 MOUNTEBANK   11 OLOROSO   12 GERTCHA

Answer No A28   P73   Tile Overseers

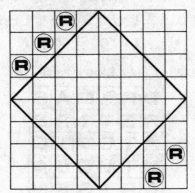

Answer No A29   P83   Hereward T. Waik
8.03a.m.

Answer No A30   P93   Roll Dem Bones Probability Theory
(i)   The odds that it will not happen are $(5/6)^4 = .482$.
Therefore the odds that it will happen are $1 - (5/6)^4 = .518$
The odds are in favour of the house 518 to 482

(ii)   The odds that it will not happen are $(35/36)^{24} = .509$
Therefore the odds that it will happen are $1 - (35/36)^{24} = .491$
The odds are in favour of the gambler. The house should say 25
throws.

Answer No A31   P4   Preposterous

Across		Down	
1 Walkway	2 Adamant	1 Cantata	2 Canasta
3 Jackass	4 Panama	3 Harass	4 Attack
5 Canal	6 Amass	5 Catamaran	6 Sadly
7 Catalyst	8 Banana	7 Alfalfa	8 Avast

Answer No A32   P14   Rabbits and Elephants
22 squares

Answer No A33   P24   The Odds On Aces
$11686/20825 \; p = 0.56115$ more than 0.5

Answer No A34   P34   Kickself Takeaway

F   I   VE   L   ET   T   ER   S

A F P I O V E L L O E T G T I E R E S S

A   P   O   L O   G   I   E S

Answer No A35   P44   A Sixer Russell Square

DRAMAS
RETIRE
ATOMIC
MIMOSA
ARISEN
SECANT

Answer No A36   P54   Twin Kickself Problems
1)   You are going to hate me. Half of each child was a boy and so was the other half. 2)   The children were not twins, they were two of a set of triplets.

Answer No A37   P64   Ingeniously Difficult
Across   *Down*
CADENCE   C A D E N C E
HOARDER   O R E D A H R
UNAIDED   D E N I D A U
PISCINE   E N I C I S P
MATTERS   S A M T R E T

They are all in the dictionary!

Answer No A38   P74   Whatever Have They Got In Common?
The 'odd one out' is PLAIT. All the rest can be diminished one letter at a time (from the beginning and the end alternately), forming a new word each time. Longer examples include aspirated, prelatess, grangers, swingers, chastens, strowing.

Answer No A39   P84   Dicing With Death
The odds were 4 to 1. There are $(5^2 \times 6) = 150$ bloody faces out of $(5^3 \times 6) = 750$ faces altogether. 600 bloodless faces against 150 sanguinary ones. Odds 4 to 1 probability 0.25.

```
I M P E R I O U S N E S S
N . I . E . C . E . B E T
S C E N A . C . T R O N A
E . . T . I . . . N . . T
N U T . A N D R O G Y N E
S . I . . E . V . . . . S
A C C I D E N T A L I S M
T . . O . T . . . M . . A
E N C O M I A S T . P E N
N . R . L . I . . . . . L
E L E C T . I . D E L H I
S E E . A . S . E . O . K
S U P E R S E N S I B L E
```

Answer No A41   P5   Animal Collections

BLAST of HUNTERS

STALK of FORESTERS

COLONY of BADGERS

CONVOCATION of EAGLES

TIDING of MAGPIES

NIDE of PHEASANT

CLOUD of SEAFOWL

SORD of MALLARD

COVERT of COOTS

DESERT of LAPWING

HERD of SWANS

BUILDING of ROOKS

SKULK of FRIARS

Answer No A42   P15   The Long Arm of Coincidence
The odds are more than fair. Ignoring February 29th you would win on average 54 times out of 100 times you bet that there would be at least one birthday coincidence among 24 people.

Answer No A43   P25   In The Proper Order
1) N   They are the initials of the number Five Ten Fifteen etc.
2) N   They are the last letters of the numbers onE twO threE, etc. 3) 11   on the bottom row. The top row are the three letter numbers one two six etc.

Answer No A44 P35 Making Big Problems Out Of Little Problems

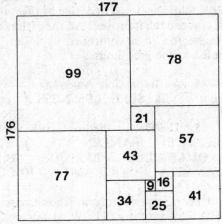

Answer No A45   P45 Gather Ye Mensans While Ye May
Bill's wife was ANN. The speaker on hypnosis was JOE.

Answer No A46   P55 A Respectful Motionless Golfer
The needle swings 4″ on its arm.

Answer No A47   P65 I Give Crossword. You Work Out Pattern

I	N	D	I	V	I	D	U	A	L	I	S	T
N	▨	R	▨	E	R	E	▨	I	▨	N	▨	H
F	L	E	U	R	E	T	▨	R	E	V	U	E
I	▨	A	▨	G	▨	E	▨	A	▨	A	▨	R
N	U	R	S	E	▨	R	H	A	B	D	O	M
E	▨	E	▨	I	▨	I	▨	E	▨	O	▨	O
T	H	R	E	E	C	O	R	N	E	R	E	D
E	▨	E	▨	F	▨	R	▨	R	▨	R	▨	Y
S	A	G	I	T	T	A	▨	S	A	P	A	N
I	▨	R	▨	▨	T	▨	W	▨	H	▨	▨	A
M	O	O	S	E	▨	I	R	I	D	I	U	M
A	▨	U	▨	G	▨	V	I	S	▨	A	▨	I
L	E	P	T	O	C	E	P	H	A	L	I	C

Answer No A48   P75   My Icosahedron's Infestation
There are 30 edges. But the yukky little horror could not traverse
them directly. It would have to go over five of them twice so I had
just 35 minutes. Not enough it proved! All the officer could do was
destroy the icosahedron in a controlled explosion in the back
garden. It demolished the greenhouse.

Answer No A49   P85   An Impossible Anagram
1) Obviously not!   2) SLEEPLESSNESS.

Answer No A50   P95   The Devil's Picture Cards
EUCHRE   ECARTE   FANTAN   PICQUET
CRIBBAGE   QUADRILLE   BEZIQUE   PINOCLE
RUMMY   CANASTA   SOLITAIRE   BACCARAT

Answer No A50B   P12   Kickself Problem Class Consciousness
The Kick BOTH ankles answer is 'H'. What was smudged over in
the answer to 12 Part 1? *Upside down* and *reversed*. They are
simple ideas but there are wheels within wheels, complications.
There are two ways to reverse a letter vertically. You can swivel it
(like a music disc) or flip it (like a pancake). In Part 1 of the
question the set of letters would only survive swivelling, turning in
the plane of the paper. You have to be very very careful. The set
B C D E H I K O X can be flipped vertically and remain the
same.

Answer No A51   P6   Improbable Sequences or Word Surgery
English words: There are, of course, many solutions to this
problem. One set of answers is: manUFActure, aNXious, sCYThe,
aCKNowledge, pYRRhic, bOOKKEEper, aWKWard, on YX.

Answer No A52   P16   Graffiti
There were eight of them. The large wall took half a gang-day in
the morning and quarter of a gang-day in the afternoon. Three
quarters. So the small wall took half that, three eighths of a gang-
day. One and one eighth gang-days altogether. There was one
eighth of a gang-day left to do and one youth did it in a day. So
the gang was eight.

Answer No A53   P26   Odd One Out
CASSINO

244

Answer No A54 P36 Cubes and Double Cubes
You can work out that there are 27 cubes altogether and that 13 will be white and 14 black. So the odd single cube must be black. As to where it goes. It can go anywhere in the large cube. If you designated particular place you were WRONG!

Answer No A55 P46 Chance Breaks
1 chance in 4. If we take any point in the large triangle, the point must fall within the shaded triangle for the three pieces to form a triangle.

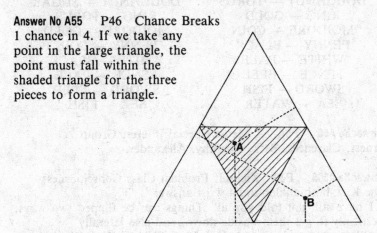

Answer No A56 P56 Space Race Base
The first two statements are true, the last two are false. The base is 9.

Answer No A57 P66 Look at it Which Way You Like

Answer No A58 P76 Maritime Variety Reduction
YAWL   XEBEC   SCHOONER   FELUCCA
WINDJAMMER   FREIGHTER
QUINQUEREME   GALLEON   BUMBOAT
CATAMARAN   GONDOLA   PINNACE

Answer No A59   P86   Semantic Dualism

SOLUTION 1	SOLUTION 2
TAP — ROOT	TAP — WATER
BEET — SUGAR	BEET — ROOT
DOUGHNUT — TORUS	DOUGHNUT — SUGAR
RING — GOLD	RING — TORUS
MOIDORE — COIN	MOIDORE — GOLD
PENNY — BLACK	PENNY — COIN
WHITE — PALE	WHITE — BLACK
FENCE — EPEE	FENCE — PALE
SWORD — FISH	SWORD — EPEE
SEA — WATER	SEA — FISH

Answer No A60   P96   A Mensa Special Interest Group
Ernest, Clarences, Beth, Dorothy, Alexander.

Answer No A60B   P12   Kickself Problem Class Consciousness
The Kick-both-ankles-and-a-wrist answer is 'T'.

I have still not told you all. Things can be flipped two ways.
Vertically to get them upside down, and also laterally.

'T' completes the set 'A H I M O T U V W X Y' that can
be flipped laterally without change.

Answer No A61   P7   Russell Square

Answer No A62   P17   The Coefficient of Expansion of Zilch?
The hole expands as though it were full of metal. It will be
10mm × 10 degrees × 0.000012 larger or 10.0012 mm in diameter. If
this looks unlikely it is easier to see if you think of a much larger
hole. At the limit you have a steel tyre such as used to be shrunken
on to a wooden wheel, by cooling hot metal.

Answer No A63   P27   How Many Books Make a Library?
One of the books must have no words at all. Suppose I had 4 books. They would have to have 3, 2, 1 and 0 words to meet the absurd conditions.

Answer No A64   P37   Backseat Driving and D.I.Y.
Doit needed 324 tiles, 3 inches square.

Answer No A65   P47   Pawnees and Queenies
He chose 2) (Stronger Weaker Stronger) because, in 1) he loses if he does not win the middle game. In 2) he has two chances against stronger players instead of one must-win one. He won and the Mensan was furious. It was a big bet.

Answer No A66   P57   The Case of the Weeping Policeman
What the pensioner lost was the 11 pounds he spent on the radio and the ten pounds he gave the thief. He failed to gain the four pounds profit he hoped for. He did not lose it.

Answer No A67   P67   Feydau Farce Puzzle
OCEANOGRAPHICAL

Answer No A68   P77   Russell Square Manes

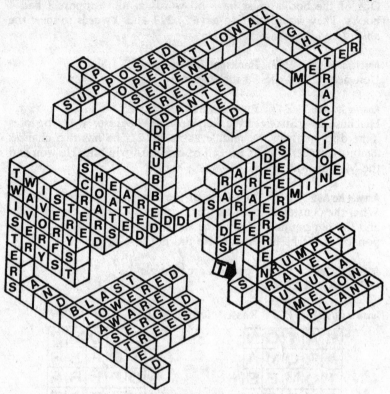

Set 9 is wrong. The first figures of all other sets are divisible by 17. The third figures are all odd and are primes. The fourth are divisible by 45. Except set 9.

248

Answer No A71   P8   Nursery Tales at my Mother's Knee

D	I	A	M	O	N	D
E		P		R		U
C	A	R	D	I	A	C
O		I		G		H
D	U	C	T	I	L	E
E		O		N		S
D	E	T	E	S	T	S

Answer No A72   P18   Kickself Calendice

DICE No 1	DICE No 2
0	0
6 serves as 9	1
7	2
8	

The lateral-think is to use the 6 upside down.

Answer No A73   P28   The Nursery Crossword

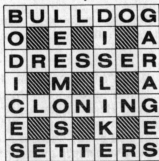

B	U	L	L	D	O	G
O		E		I		A
D	R	E	S	S	E	R
I		M		L		A
C	L	O	N	I	N	G
E		S		K		E
S	E	T	T	E	R	S

Answer No A74   P38   Topological Nonsense Object

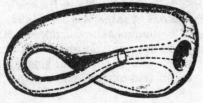

It is that topological freak the Klein Bottle and you can blame the German Mathematician Felix Klein for inventing it. He took a glass tube, drew out one end like a neck, turned it back inside the tube, brought it out through the side of the tube expanded it and joined it to the other end of the tube. That made the inside face continuous with the outside face. If you worked this one out without having heard of the Klein Bottle you get a Cartload of Chalks.

Answer No A75   P48   Kickself Problem for Daily Amputees
No-one shaves the Barber. She was the Mayor's wife.

Answer No A76   P58   The Biggest Niff

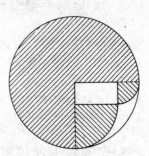

¾ of original circle—   1039½ s.f.
¼ of circle radius 14 feet—   154 s.f.
¼ of circle radius 7 feet—   38½ s.f.
                               1232 s.f.
Original circle   1386 s.f.
Grazing 1232/1386 = 88.8% × £100
Should pay   £88.80
Reduction   £11.20

Answer No A77   P68   Chancing it with Octahedral Dice
The best way to visualise an octohedron is to think of two five faced pyramids joined at the square bases. The odds would be 5 chances in 64, probability, $p = 0.078125$, you could nearly afford to pay 13 to 1.

Answer No A78   P78   Watch Out or You'll Be Late
Julie gets there first, and is furious when the train comes in and leaves before Tim arrives. He had allowed five for his clock but 6.05 by his clock is 6.15 out in the harsh world of real time. The angry Julie, arriving at 5.50 by her watch is pacing up and down from 4.45 to 6.15. She lost her temper and slapped his face. He was surprised. But more surprised than pleased.

Answer No A79   P88   Kickself Mr Nasty Parker
Mr Nasty Parker was one of three who came later. He occupied an empty space, took a summons from under another windscreen wiper and put it under his own. So one of the cars got a second summons and the trick was revealed. But giggling, unpleasant Mr Nasty Parker was gone and untraceable.

Answer No A80   P98   A Family Party
The Party will be attended by Mary and her three guests. Mary's
sister is married to Mary's husband's brother. The mother of both
men happens to be Mary's mother's sister and to be married to
Mary's paternal uncle. There are incestuous or illegal relationships.
The neighbour? Her sister.

Answer No A81   P9   The Labyrinth
UNINTENTIONALLY

Answer No A82   P19   Having the Balls to Take a Chance
Here are the calculations.

a) $^{20}/_{50} \times ^{30}/_{49} = ^{600}/_{2450}$ 1850 to 600
b) $^{30}/_{50} \times ^{20}/_{49} = ^{600}/_{2450}$ 1850 to 600
c) $^{20}/_{50} \times ^{19}/_{49} = ^{380}/_{2450}$ 2070 to 380
d) $^{30}/_{50} \times ^{29}/_{49} = ^{870}/_{2450}$ 1580 to 870

Answer No A83   P29   Recognition Problem 1
The message was simple. The spaces between the hedges spell out
the word 'HELLO.'

Answer No A84   P39   Romance and Tragedy
P39A   The Slugs Adventurous Romance
If you get it congratulations indeed! The shape has no name as far
as I know and you can call it a Serebriakoff Torus or a One-face
Hollow Torus if you like. It has one surface and its inside,
alternately, is its outside. And vice versa.

The Klein Bottle has no inside, no outside, and only one surface.
The three stage One-face Hollow Torus has similar properties.

As you will see a tube is narrowed, retroverted and passed through its wall, Klein style, and joined to another tube which is treated alike at its other end. The third links similarly to the first. Viola! Object S! The inside of one sausage or bottle is the outside of the next and vice versa. The slugs go outside then inside without leaving the smoothly curving wall.

When the worn out female halted in a neck, the male came by on the same side of the glass after his next circuit.

P39B   The Slugs Tragic Passionate Celibacy
The difference was very little. Object X was hollow torus but it had two sections instead of three. that made it a Two Faced Hollow Torus with interchanging faces as shown in the diagram. It has two separate realms within its continuity boundaries. Both the slugs went alternatively inside and outside as before but they could never be inside or outside the same section as the loved one.

Chains of these surface reversing torus sections of any number of stages can be made. Those with an even number of stages are X-like. Those with an odd number are S-like.

Answer No A85   P49   The Chance of a Deal
They favour the dealer. $p = 0.5588$ that neither will be of named suit
Will not $^{39}/_{52} \times {}^{38}/_{51} = {}^{1482}/_{2652} = 55.88\%$

Will 44.12%.

Answer No A86   P59   How Many Chess Sets?
There are just 108 089 907 200 ways. At one a minute, working a forty hour week it would take about one and two thirds million years. Boring is what it would be.

Answer No A87   P69   Do You Love Jesus?
1 CAMEMBERT   2 GORGONZOLA
3 EMMENTHAL   4 ROQUEFORT   5 GERVAS
6 TILSITER   7 GRUYERE   8 REBLOCHON
9 CHESHIRE   10 PARMESAN
11 LIMBURGER   12 GOUDA

STRAIGHTFORWARD

Answer No A89   P89   Followordirectionotypical
1 GARDENIAS   2 SCALLYWAG   3 GATHERING
4 GEOMETER   5 RELEVANT   6 TANGRAM
7 MARVELS   8 SABOT   9 THERMOS
10 SUSPECT   11 TIGRESS   12 SLIP   13 PARES
14 SIP   15 PENT   16 THIN   17 NUT

Answer No A90   P99   The Aged Mensan Tycoon

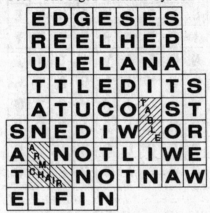

E	D	G	E	S	E	S	
R	E	E	L	H	E	P	
U	L	E	L	A	N	A	
T	T	L	E	D	I	T	S
A	T	U	C	O	T/ABLE	S	T
S	N	E	D	I	W	E	O	R
A	ARM	N	O	T	L	I	W	E
T	CHAIR	N	O	T	N	A	W
E	L	F	I	N

Answer No A91   P10   Writing Two PI Plus

M¹	E⁵	S	I	O	T	R	O	T⁴
M¹⁰	I	C¹³	M	A	E	S	N¹²	S⁷
A	I	N	O	I	D	E	P	S
S	S¹⁷	R	I	N	M	L	M¹⁵	A
C	I	L	E	A	O	E	U	R
A	P	P	E	T	T	M	S¹⁴	I
R	P	N	C	E¹⁶	N	U	I	U
A¹¹	I	H⁸	O	U	R	I⁹	R	C⁶
L³	A	R	E	M	E	H	P	E²

Answer No A92   P20   Bird Bush Tree
1) FULMAR, ASPEN and TIT. 2) HERON and CEDAR.
3) CHOUGH and ELM.

Answer No A93   P30   Recognition Problem 2
It was simply a glass door with 'PUSH' on one side and 'PULL'
on the other.

Answer No A94   P40   He Rode Off In All Directions

P	T	S	I	P	P	A	R	T
S	A	R	A	V	O	N	N	E
I	F	R	A	R	E	E	N	V
N	G	F	A	V	I	T	R	A
C	U	N	I	L	E	A	I	R
E	N	L	I	R	Y	R	S	G
R	N	S	I	S	A	S	S	N
E	E	C	L	O	U	T	I	E
R	O	T	A	T	C	E	P	S

Answer No A95   P50   Order! Order!
We are only interested in the top 4 cards which for convenience we
can call 1-2-3-4. There are only 24 ways in which the 4 cards can
fall, only one of which will be in ascendancy. The chances are
therefore 1 in 24.

Answer No A96   P60   All Only Now Quickly

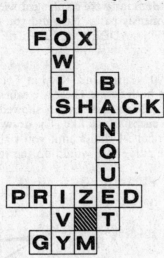

Answer No A97   P70   A Bit Out
By extending the lines of Tom's claim on Lem's land as shown it became obvious that the 4 sections thus delineated were equal and that the disputed area was a quarter of Lem's claim so that Tom should have an eighth of the yield of the mine.

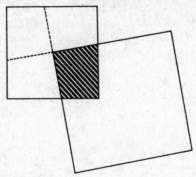

Answer No A98   P80   Whoppers
George has ten fish, Henry twelve, and Michael nine.

Answer No A99   P90   Name Punched in Metal

Thirteen thousand Mensans were challenged with this and all that came in were three measly pairs. How did you do? Here they are SHEER AND TIFFS, ADDER AND BEEFS, SNEER AND TOFFS.

Answer No A100   P100   Turn Line. Keep in Touch.

The answer is yes in both cases. These are called a deltoid curves. The mathematician Abram Besicovitch showed that such curves could have as many cusps as you like. The drawings illustrate. The formula is very difficult. I shall count you right if you saw that there was a concave curve that would do the job.

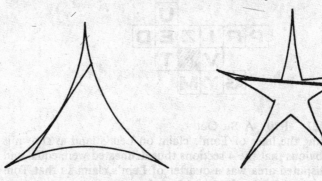